electronic hobbyists' handbook

rufus p. turner
Registered Professional Engineer

GERNSBACK LIBRARY INC.
NEW YORK 11, N. Y.

Library of Congress Catalog Card No. 57—9010

contents

Introduction

ELECTRONIC experimenters come from many walks of life. Some are employed in the electronics industry, yet derive exhilaration from spare-time activities along the same line. Others follow occupations which are not even remotely connected with electronics. All have the common goal of personal delight and enlightenment. Significant inventions have come from their home workshops and laboratories.

This book is a collection of practical circuits for the electronic experimenter. I believe he will find between its covers many hookups he will want to try. I have checked them all. Some experimenters will want to tie some of the circuits together, like building blocks, to form systems of their own.

The circuits have been grouped into chapters, each of which is devoted to a "family" of similar circuits. This arrangement will enable the reader to locate more quickly the kind of circuit he needs. For the benefit of the newcomer, a certain amount of space also has been devoted to workshop practice.

There is bound to be some disagreement as to what should be included in a book of this type. Many a reader will regret that some favorite topic is omitted. But there has not been room for everything. In my selection, I have been influenced to some extent by my own interests. But in the final choice of topics, I have also paid particular attention to the kind of information most often asked for in letters from the readers of my magazine articles.

To the reader, I wish many happy and profitable hours of experimentation—and boundless inspiration.

RUFUS P. TURNER,
Los Angeles, California.

Abbreviations Used In This Book

amp	ampere (s)	L	inductance
ac	alternating current	lf	low frequency
af	audio frequency	L-C	inductance-
AM	amplitude modulation		capacitance
	or -modulated	lv	low voltage
ant	antenna		
AWG	American Wire Gauge	M	meter
		mc	megacycle (s)
B & S	Brown & Sharpe	mega	prefix meaning
			1,000,000 times
C	capacitance	mh	millihenry
C1, C2, etc.	capacitors	micro	prefix meaning
CW	continuous wave (s)		1-millionth
cps	cycles per second	mike	microphone
		milli	prefix meaning
db	decibel (s)		1-thousandth
dc	direct current	μf	microfarad (s)
dpdt	double-pole,	μh	microhenry (ies)
	double-throw switch	$\mu\mu f$	micromicrofarad (s)
dpst	double-pole,	μv	microvolt (s)
	single-throw switch	ma	milliampere (s)
		mv	millivolt (s)
E	voltage	mw	milliwatt (s)
emf	electromotive force		
		osc	oscillator
f	frequency	Out	output
FM	frequency-modulation		
	or -modulated	PA	public address
		pf	power factor
gain cont	gain control	pot	potentiometer
gnd	ground		
		R	resistance
h	henry (ies)	R1, R2, etc.	resistors
hf	high frequency	R-C	resistance-capacitance
hv	high voltage	reg	regulated
		R_L	load resistance
I	current	rf	radio frequency
if	intermediate		
	frequency	S	switch
In	input	scope	oscilloscope
		spkr	speaker or loudspeaker
kc	kilocycle (s)	spdt	single-pole,
kilo	prefix meaning		double-throw switch
	1,000 times	spst	single-pole,
kv	kilovolt (s)		single-throw switch
kw	kilowatt (s)		

Abbreviations Used In This Book

T	transformer	vtvm	vacuum-tube voltmeter
uhf	ultra high frequency		
		w	watt (s)
v	volt (s)	ww	wirewound
V1, V2, etc.	tube or transistor		
vhf	very high frequency	X	reactance
vol cont	volume control	xtal	quartz crystal
vom	volt-ohm-milliammeter		
V-R	voltage regulated	Z	impedance

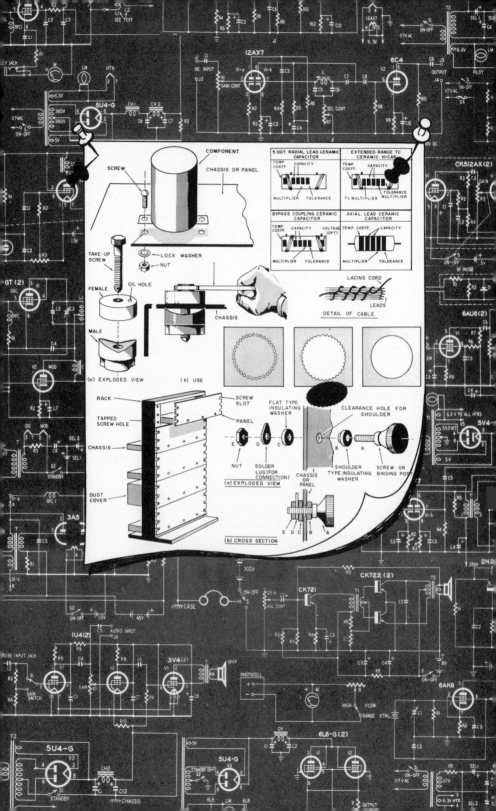

safety in electronics

ELECTRICITY is a wonderful servant and a great hobby. But it can hurt and even kill you if you grow careless with it. Learn the rules of safety early in the game and follow them faithfully for the rest of your life.

Many people think that only large amounts of electricity are harmful; that is, high voltages and high currents. They scoff at anything under 200 volts. But small amounts are just as dangerous when they hit in the right place! A tiny shock, under certain conditions, can cause a reflex action that will stop your heart. Other people expect great knowledge alone to protect them. But they are wrong. Too often we read that some well-trained technician with many years of experience has been accidentally electrocuted. It takes only a split second to come to grief, and death is so permanent.

These remarks are not intended to alarm the reader nor to frighten people away from electronics. Our aim is to protect you by pointing out the danger spots. Other hobbies also have their potential dangers. Chemistry, for example, is another fine hobby. But one must be careful with it too, otherwise there is the possibility of being poisoned, gassed or blown to bits.

The rules of conduct around electrical equipment are simple and easy to follow. The important ones are outlined in the following paragraphs. Read them several times until you know them thoroughly and decide to make them your good habits.

Avoid shock

This is the first safety rule. Don't expose yourself foolishly. There is nothing manly about being "able to take it." Even mild shocks for the fun of it have been known to cause physical or mental trouble several months or even several years after the shock was received. Don't take our word for this—examine the medical records.

When you are testing electronic equipment that is in operation, don't touch live parts with any part of your body. And never, never touch any equipment with more than one part of your body simultaneously—like both hands, one hand and one leg, etc. PRACTICE THE COMMON-SENSE RULE OF KEEPING ONE HAND IN YOUR POCKET. In this way, if you should accidentally receive a shock, the current will not flow through one of your vital organs. Become a one-handed electronic tester and you will live long to enjoy your hobby.

Know the circuit

Before delving into any electronic equipment, study the circuit carefully. If you don't have a circuit diagram, wait until one arrives before starting work. Learn the operation of the device and something about the voltages to be expected at various points in the circuit. Unfamiliarity with the equipment and its operating theory invites danger.

Plan your work

Know exactly what steps you are going to take, before you start testing a circuit. In your mind, rehearse the full program before you pick up a tool. And know pretty well what kind of results to expect. Never tackle strange equipment without this preparation.

One medical authority on electric shock has said that much of the damage is caused by the sudden surprise. This does not mean that you should go about your work so tensed that you expect to be floored any second. Your hobby soon would become a nightmare. But you can realize ahead of time that you are going to be stung if you touch certain "hot" parts of the equipment. It is a case of forewarned is forearmed.

Be a switch-off man

Some operators like to replace parts with the power turned on. They think that "working the circuit hot" allows them to observe more quickly what changes take place in operation of the equipment. That might be so, but your life and health are worth more than the added time required for safety. It only takes a second to shut the power off before you work on your apparatus.

Have company

It is wrong to work alone. If you should be badly shocked, there would be no one to give first aid, switch off the power and call a doctor. At all times, but especially when you are working with high-voltage equipment, have another person around who knows how to disable the equipment and who can give artificial respiration in case of shock. This author knows of a case where a technician was knocked unconscious by high voltage and upon regaining his senses many hours later discovered that during his blackout the soldering iron had burned its way through the workbench. This man was doubly lucky that he wasn't electrocuted and that the house was not burned down.

Ground your equipment

Connect all power-line-operated electronic equipment and electric tools to a good earth ground. In any city, you can get a good ground by connecting a heavy wire solidly to the cold water pipe. In other locations, drive a long metal rod or pipe deep into moist earth and connect the ground wire to it.

First-class electric drills and similar tools are provided with a ground lead on the plug end of their power cords. Use this lead for grounding, as it was intended. Don't snip it off because "it is in the way."

Avoid personal grounds

Many a strong man has been electrocuted when he became grounded through his feet. If you are working with electronic equipment or using electric tools, don't stand on the ground or on a cellar floor. If your workshop is in the cellar or garage, make yourself a dry wood platform to stand on or use a rubber mat— or wear rubbers.

It is stupid to work with electricity outdoors barefooted. Still, we read regularly about people being shocked to death while operating car waxers, hedge clippers, ac–dc radios and electric lawn mowers in their bare feet. Toss your house slippers into the closet and put on stout shoes when you work with electricity.

Take a look at experienced electricians and old-timers in industrial plants. They wear shoes with thick rubber soles. You couldn't pay these men to wear thin-soled dress shoes on the job.

A very good way to ground your body is to sit in a bathtub full of water. Make it a habit to leave your electronic gear and your radio outside when you take a bath. Draw a sharp line between bath time and work time. Only a miracle could save you if you touched a short-circuited power-line-operated device while sitting in a full tub.

Be high-voltage alert

When working with high-voltage equipment, keep your full attention on what you are doing. If you must daydream, gripe, chat with someone or gaze elsewhere, then close shop and come back at some later time when you can give undivided attention to the job.

Around high voltage, you won't be a sissy (no matter who says so) if you wear rubber gloves. It always is sensible to protect yourself.

Discharge capacitors

Capacitors are so deadly because they are simple and look so innocent. A capacitor has been known to hold a murderous charge several days after the voltage has been shut down.

An excellent habit is to short-circuit each capacitor several times with an insulated-handle screwdriver or rod before working on any equipment which has been in operation.

In general, the higher the capacitance and the better the quality of the capacitor, the more dangerous this component is apt to be. But don't trust any of them. It is good practice to put a "bleeder" resistor across filter capacitors.

Watch choke coils

A large choke coil is deceptive because it is likely to deliver a nasty jolt as the current is being turned off. Don't touch choke-coil terminals until you know for sure that the power already is off.

Beware the power line

The ac power line is bad medicine. The frequency is just right to throw your heart out of kilter. There are people who have no respect whatever for 115 volts ac. But, be assured, it has laid many a person low. Equipment operated directly from the power line without an isolating transformer is particularly dangerous. Be careful how you handle it.

Never use your fingers to determine if the power is on. This is a fool's trick. You could be killed if another part of your body became grounded at the same time.

Don't play

Electronics is an enjoyable hobby. But electricity also is a serious business. Enjoy it but don't play with it. Nothing is accomplished by drawing sparks, making short circuits and such shenanigans. But you invite a lot of danger when you play in this manner. Outlaw practical jokes. Don't use electricity or electronic equipment for horse play. Never shock another person (especially when he doesn't know it is coming) or cause him to fall into, jump into or grasp any part of electrical equipment.

Quit when tired

Fatigue is bad for two reasons. You are nowhere near alert enough or quick on the jump when you are tired. The other reason is that a tired man is a pushover for injurious electric shock. His body is at low pitch.

To be tired and sweating at the same time is a really bad combination. Perspiration makes your skin a good conductor of electricity and increases your chances of being hurt.

Regarding the amount of work, know when you have had enough and know enough to call it a day.

Restore equipment completely

When you have taken a piece of equipment apart for repairs, put it back together into its original shape. Replace every nut, screw and washer, and especially insulating washers and separators. Transformerless equipment, such as ac–dc radios, TV sets, intercoms and similar devices often are housed in metal cases and have insulators to keep the hot chassis safely separated from the case. The manufacturer has provided this safety feature. When you fail to replace such insulators, you expose yourself or other users to dangerous electric shock. Never replace the plastic or wooden knobs of such equipment with metal ones.

Before installing a chassis in a cabinet, examine all parts of the circuit for particles of solder which may have dripped into the wiring. Such particles can cause short circuits and are fire hazards as well as shock hazards.

Never replace a component with a lighter-duty one. Undersized components heat up in use and can cause fires as well as additional electrical trouble. When in doubt, install an oversized component.

Install equipment sensibly

Install all electrical equipment with safety in mind. Use door or cover switches on cabinets housing high-voltage apparatus so that the power will be switched off automatically when the door is opened or cover lifted. Keep your equipment integral whenever possible—that is, do not have a power supply in one place and the equipment it operates in another place with wires running between. In permanent installations requiring wiring to the power line make all connections in accordance with local electrical regulations. Or, better still, have this work done by an experienced electrician.

Take extra precautions when the equipment you work on is to be operated by persons less experienced than yourself. Never locate apparatus near water pipes or radiators where a child or an inexperienced adult might contact the grounded pipe at the same time he touches the equipment. An example of a poor installation is an ac–dc radio or intercom (or a metal-cased, transformerless TV) directly over a kitchen sink.

shop practice

IT is as true in the construction of electronic equipment as in any other type of building that a job can be done faster and with the least fatigue and annoyance to the worker if the correct tools are used and if they are kept in good condition.

Certain special tools enable the technician to do particular jobs with greater ease than with ordinary tools. However, such tools usually cost more than conventional ones and their ownership is a luxury unless they are used often. It would hardly be feasible, for example, to install a labor-saving but expensive drill press if only half a dozen holes are to be drilled in a year.

This brings up the point that certain tools are absolutely essential for electronic construction while others are desirable but dispensable. Still others are recommended only when a large amount of equipment building is being done constantly, especially on a commercial basis. Table A lists the hand tools which are essential in the building of electronic gear. Table B shows certain additional tools and equipment which will facilitate work. Table C gives still more extra tools and equipment which would make for a well-rounded shop but constitute a needless expense to the experimenter who builds a piece of equipment only occasionally. Advanced machine tools, like the lathe and miller, are of no direct value in electronic construction unless special mechanical components and fittings are built regularly and the technician is in some form of manufacturing.

Under certain circumstances, even the list of essential tools in Table A may be abbreviated. For example, in the building of very simple devices requiring no cutting or drilling and in the construction of kit type instruments in which all of the metal cutting has been done by the manufacturer, the builder can get along with only pliers, diagonal cutters, screwdriver, soldering iron and knife. Furthermore, since no heavy construction is required, all of the work can be done on a card table if a workbench is not available.

In compiling the tool lists, it has been assumed that the reader already has such basic materials as sandpaper, steel wool, wiping rags, rosin-core solder, can of oil, touchup paint, etc. that might be used in any household job a handyman is called upon to do.

Tools are sold at various prices. The wide selection is certain to raise in the mind of the experimenter some question as to how much he should pay. With few exceptions, both cheap and ex-

Table A—ESSENTIAL TOOLS

1 6-inch long-nose pliers
1 6-inch diagonal cutters
1 Heavy (gas-pipe) pliers
1 Hacksaw, with blades
1 Coping saw, with blades (preferably spiral type)
1 Long-blade screwdriver
1 Short-blade screwdriver
1 Adjustable open-end wrench
1 Ball-peen hammer
1 $\frac{1}{4}$-inch hand or electric drill
1 Set of drills (spaced in 64ths from $\frac{1}{16}$ to $\frac{1}{4}$ inch)
1 100-watt soldering iron or gun
5 Screw-type socket punches ($\frac{5}{8}$, $\frac{3}{4}$, 1, $1\frac{1}{8}$, and $1\frac{1}{4}$ inches)
1 Combination steel square and rule
1 Scriber or scratch awl
1 Set of files. Assorted large and medium sizes, coarse and fine (flat, round and half-round)
1 Center punch
1 File brush
1 Knife, electrician's or Boy Scout
1 Pair steel dividers
1 $\frac{1}{2}$-inch taper reamer (fine tip, $\frac{1}{16}$ inch)
1 Cold chisel
1 Oil stone
1 Paint brush, $1\frac{1}{4}$ inch minimum width, for dusting

pensive tools usually will do the same job equally well. But the expensive tool by lasting a longer time, will be more economical than the cheap one. A good rule, therefore, is to buy top-grade tools if you expect to keep busy building equipment for some time, but inexpensive ones if your activity is very limited. The cheaper tools, used infrequently, should last quite as long as the more expensive tool which is subjected to a heavy work load.

Table B—DESIRABLE ADDITIONAL TOOLS

1 Workbench. Suggested minimum size: 6 feet long, 3 feet wide
1 Heavy-duty vise
1 Wire stripper
1 Carpenter's brace
1 Set of taps and dies
1 Set of Phillips screwdrivers
1 Set of Allen wrenches
1 Set of socket wrenches (Spintites)
1 Set of flat, open-end wrenches
1 Steel tape
1 Pair tinner's snips
1 Pair scissors or shears
1 Pair tweezers or forceps
1 Countersink
1 Soldering aid

Table C—DE LUXE ADDITIONAL TOOLS

1 Drill press. $\frac{1}{2}$-inch maximum chuck size
1 Bench saw
1 Complete set of drills (up to $\frac{1}{2}$ inch)
1 Drill vise
1 Motor-driven grinder
1 Blow torch
1 Spray gun
1 Heavy-duty soldering iron (200 watts minimum)
1 Set of screw-type punches for rectangular, D-shaped and keyed holes
1 Adjustable circle cutter
1 Set of miniature screwdrivers
1 Set of metal C-clamps
1 1-inch micrometer
1 3-corner scraper
1 Wire gauge
1 Drill and tap gauge

Care of tools

The effectiveness of tools and their useful life depend a great deal upon the care they receive. Although the electronic technician is not primarily a mechanic, he should not be ignorant of tool care and he should cultivate good tool habits.

Intelligent handling

A tool should not be used beyond its capacity. If, for example, a light saw is used to cut heavy stock, its blade is sure to be dulled or broken. A knife should not be used as a cold chisel. Cutting tools must not be allowed to overheat during use.

Tools should be grasped firmly so that they will not be dropped and their edges chipped or blunted. The good mechanic handles himself in a workmanlike manner, realizing that he must concentrate on the job and on protection of his tools. He knows that his shop is not the place to daydream or dawdle.

Protection

Since many tools are made of steel, they are subject to rust. Take every precaution to prevent rusting. If tools are used very seldom or if the shop is damp, they should be protected with a light film of oil. Usually, an occasional thorough wiping with an oily rag will suffice.

Tools also must be protected from dust, dirt and grit. If it has been necessary for them to lie on the ground, they should be wiped clean before being put away. They always should be kept in a dust-tight enclosure when not in use.

Use every precaution to protect sharp-edged tools from damage by falling or striking against each other and other objects. If kept in a drawer or tool box, they should be arranged in such a way that they will not bounce about. Protect pointed tools, like awls, scribes and dividers, by pressing a small cork or pencil eraser over each point.

Sharpening

Resharpen edged and pointed tools frequently. This includes drills, scribers, chisels and knives. Although a good bench grinder is invaluable, you need not go to this expense if you cannot afford the machine and if you will use an oil stone intelligently.

Cleaning

Tools should not be allowed to remain clogged. Metal burrs

and chips, impacted wood or plastic, and grease should be cleaned away carefully before a tool is put away. After each work period, files should be worked over briskly with a file brush to remove jammed materials from between the ridges. Do not delay this chore. Nothing is more demoralizing than a clogged or dirty tool.

Lubricating

Keep all "moving" tools sufficiently, but not excessively, lubricated. Give the right amount of oiling to drills and other machines. This also applies to hand-squeezed tools like pliers, cutters, nippers, wire strippers, scissors, snips, etc.

Soldering-iron care

Keep the tip of your soldering iron well tinned and clean. Do not allow the iron to heat for long idle periods without wiping the tip frequently with a clean, dry cloth, otherwise severe oxidation will occur. Guard against overheating. If you do a lot of soldering, remove the tip at least once a week and shake the accumulated slag out of the socket. If this is not done, the tip eventually will bind so tightly that it cannot be removed.

If you use a soldering gun, do not keep the trigger depressed for prolonged periods. The gun overheats unless reasonable cooling intervals are allowed between the heatings. Usually a few seconds to a minute of time will suffice between uses. Store the gun in such a way that the tip does not become bent.

Types of construction

The construction of experimental electronic equipment, such as might be built by the hobbyist, takes six familiar forms: breadboard, open chassis, chassis and panel, enclosed cabinet, rack and panel and utility box. The particular form selected depends upon individual requirements and the need for permanence. Each form is described separately in the following paragraphs.

Breadboard

In this type of construction, the electrical components are mounted on the top face of a wooden board, hence the name breadboard. Usually, the connecting wires simply are run along the top of the board from one component to another. But sometimes, for improved appearance, a lead will be partially concealed by running it from one component, through a hole in the board, and then along the bottom of the board to another hole through which it is passed to a second component.

Fig. 201 shows typical breadboard construction. The components are most easily fastened to the board with wood screws. Machine screws and nuts also can be used, but this necessitates drilling holes for the screws. The screws pass through hollow studs or pillars to hold components like tube sockets above the board. Note that the fixed capacitor in the illustration is held by its pigtail leads, which are soldered to the two lugs of a terminal strip screwed to the board. Lead A is run directly from the choke to a tube socket terminal while lead B is conducted part of the way under the board for concealment.

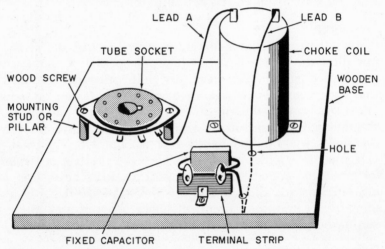

Fig. 201. *Typical breadboard construction.*

Fig. 202 shows a variation of the breadboard scheme. Here, a front panel has been added for dials, switches and other controls.

Materials other than wood occasionally are employed in breadboard type construction. They include Masonite, Celotex, bakelite and other plastics. In an emergency, a stout cardboard box has been used.

Breadboard construction allows an electronic circuit to be assembled quickly and cheaply, with fair neatness. It is very convenient for rapid preliminary tests of circuits and systems. All components and test points are easily accessible for experimentation.

Open chassis

Components may be mounted with machine screws and nuts on a metal chassis instead of a breadboard. Physically, the arrangement is identical with that of the breadboard. The general construction is the same as that shown in Figs. 201 and 202. However, the chassis has the advantages of being fireproof, more rigid in most instances and (when shielding is desired) some components may be mounted below the chassis. Furthermore, the metal chassis offers a good solid ground connection for many parts of the circuit it supports.

The advantages of the open-chassis type of construction some-

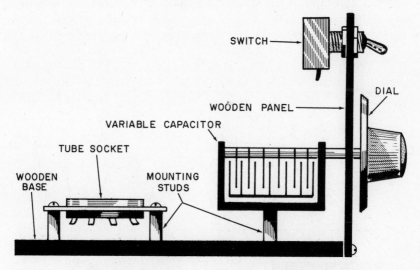

Fig. 202. *Breadboard and panel construction.*

times are overweighed by the need to drill holes for all mounting screws and also by the necessity for insulating the parts of some components that pass through the chassis.

A variation of the open-chassis scheme is the method of mounting the components to the chassis instead of on it. Clearance-holes are cut for sockets, transformers and similar parts, and all wiring is done under the chassis. Usually, this type of construction involves as much work as fabricating a complete and final instrument. However, the scheme is preferred to all others by some developmental engineers because the device more nearly approximates the finished design and very little trouble is experienced from stray coupling, lead movement and similar causes. Commercial experimental chassis are available with numerous holes and cutouts of various sizes for open-chassis work. They are relatively expensive and amateurs who do a lot of experimenting have provided a good substitute by keeping on hand a chassis precut with a number of socket, transformer and miscellaneous holes.

Chassis and panel

Like the breadboard and panel type of construction illustrated in Fig. 202, metal chassis and panel arrangements may be used. This latter technique is the one most frequently employed in the construction of experimental electronic equipment.

Two common types of metal chassis and panel construction are shown in Fig. 203: Components such as tube sockets, transformers, chokes, resistors and capacitors usually are mounted on

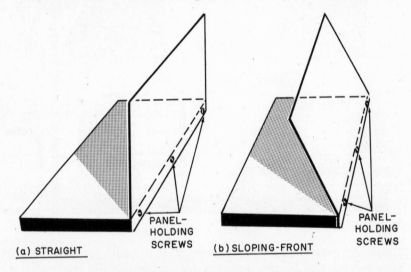

Fig. 203. *Metal chassis and panel construction.*

the chassis although some of them might be fastened to the panel as well. Indicating meters and controls, such as switches, potentiometers, rheostats and tuning capacitors, are mounted on the front panel. Principal wiring is under the chassis. Fig. 203-a illustrates the straight-panel arrangement while Fig. 203-b shows the sloping-front panel. The latter type is especially desirable in test instruments since it allows the reading of meters and dials from either a sitting or standing position.

Enclosed cabinet

A well-protected, shielded, permanent assembly is obtained when the metal chassis and panel unit is enclosed in a metal case or cabinet. This type of foundation unit is illustrated in Fig.

204. In each instance, the chassis is shown slightly withdrawn from the cabinet.

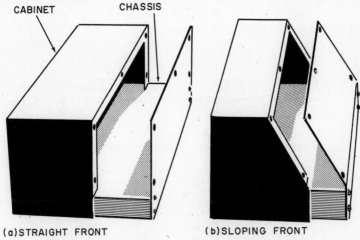

(a)STRAIGHT FRONT   (b)SLOPING FRONT

Figs. 204-a, -b. *Enclosed cabinet foundation units.*

Enclosed cabinets, with chassis, are available commercially in a wide variety of sizes which satisfy most demands of electronic construction.

Utility boxes

A large variety of small aluminum and steel boxes, with and without chassis, are available as foundation units for electronic equipment. They are to be found in radio stores and listed in radio mail-order catalogues. These boxes are particularly useful for equipment too small to fill a standard-sized chassis or cabinet. In larger equipment, the utility box is used often as a shield, an entire stage of an electronic circuit being built inside.

Rack and panel

Fig. 205 illustrates a type of foundation unit used widely, particularly in the construction of radio transmitters. This is a metal chassis and panel type of construction but the panel of each unit is held to an upright metal rack, a type of frame which supports the entire assembly. This configuration accounts for the name "rack and panel." In Fig. 205, the top panel and chassis are shown slightly withdrawn from the rack.

Screw-clearance slots are cut at regular intervals along the left and right edges of each panel. The rack has threaded screw holes spaced to match the positions of the panel slots.

Standard rack panels are 19 inches long and are available in various heights from 1¾ to 21 inches in steel or aluminum. Standard chassis are 17 inches long. Racks are available in floor sizes up to 6 feet high and in shorter table mounting sizes.

Some amateurs have built wooden racks to accommodate standard metal rack panels but most experimenters prefer to purchase this equipment.

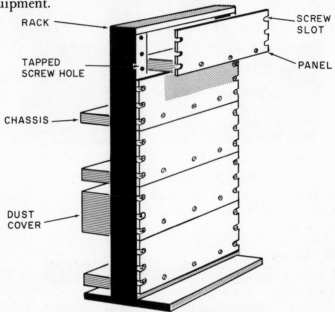

Fig. 205. *Rack and panel construction.*

Chassis may be left open in rack and panel assemblies or enclosed in metal dust covers. (See Fig. 205.) For complete enclosure and protection of the equipment, enclosed racks resembling large metal cabinets are available.

Chassis and panel working

The building of electronic equipment begins with mechanical work on chassis and panel. This section discusses the various phases of this work.

Laying out

The first step is layout. This means locating the proper positions for all components and holes. There are two common ways of doing this job. One is to make the layout directly on the actual chassis or panel. This can be done with pencil, crayon or a scriber. Use a steel square or other straightedge for drawing lines and locating points. Use a prick punch to make a point for each drill-hole location. The other method is to make the layout on a sheet of paper the same size as the chassis or panel and to prick-punch the drilling points through the paper onto the chassis.

Drilling

Clearly prick-punch each point at which a hole is to be drilled. At the punch mark, drill a short distance into the stock, first with

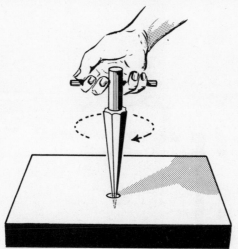

Fig. 206. *Using taper reamer to enlarge hole.*

a drill several sizes smaller than the desired hole size. This forms a pilot which keeps the larger drill from "walking" and making a ragged or displaced hole. It is not necessary to drill all the way through with the smaller drill.

For best accuracy when using the drill press, fasten the work in the drill press with clamps or use a drill-press vise. Always use clamps or a vise (or stout pliers) to hold thin sheet stock being drilled. Never hold such stock with the bare hands. There is a tendency for it to be twisted from the grip by a rapidly spinning drill press or electric drill, and serious injury can result.

Reaming

Small holes may be enlarged to diameters beyond drill size by means of a taper reamer. Fig. 206 shows the method of using this tool. A handle type reamer is shown here but others are available for use in a carpenter's brace.

Use of socket punches

Holes for tube and cable sockets, can-type electrolytic capacitors and electrical receptacles may be cut conveniently, easily and noiselessly with screw-type socket punches.

A screw-type punch has three parts: a female die, male punch and takeup screw. (See Fig. 207-a.) A clearance hole (usually ⅜ inch) for the screw is first drilled in the chassis or panel. The punch then is placed under the work, the die on top, and the

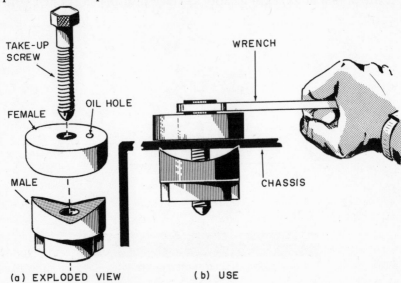

TAKE-UP SCREW
FEMALE
OIL HOLE
MALE
WRENCH
CHASSIS

(a) EXPLODED VIEW   (b) USE

Figs. 207-a, -b. *Screw-type socket punch.*

screw threaded in and finger-tightened. Then, using a wrench as shown in Fig. 207-b, the screw is tightened further until the punch bites through the metal and makes a clean hole.

Standard socket punches are available for cutting holes up to 2½ inches in diameter. There also are rectangular, D-shaped and keyed-hole varieties.

Cutting large circular holes

When a slow-speed drill press is available, an adjustable circle cutter (also called a fly cutter) can be used to cut large-diameter round holes. Such holes are required by meters, dials and some transformers. These cutters never should be used in electric drills since the high speed of the latter will cause the cutting tool to break if it should snag in the work. A flying chip from a broken tool can cause serious accidents.

When a circle cutter is not available, a large-diameter hole can be cut in the manner shown in Figs. 208 and 209. In the first illustration, a number of holes are drilled around an inscribed circle of the desired diameter (Fig. 208-a). A small cold chisel then is used to cut through the metal separations between holes. The center disk of metal then is knocked out (Fig. 208-b). The hole is toothed but can be smoothed with a half-round file (Fig. 208-c). In the second illustration (Fig. 209), only one small hole is drilled. The blade of a spiral-blade coping saw then is inserted

(a) HOLES DRILLED IN   (b) CENTER KNOCKED   (c) FILED SMOOTH
     CIRCLE   OUT

Figs. 208-a, -b, -c. *One way to cut large circular holes.*

through this hole and the large round cutout is sawed. The spiral blade has the advantage that it permits sawing in any direction at will. Thus, it is easy to saw around a circle. The scheme is simply to start at the hole and saw around the inscribed circle back to the hole, whereupon the center metal disk falls away.

Cutting large rectangular holes

The same techniques illustrated in Figs. 208 and 209 for round holes may be employed to cut rectangular and square holes required by transformers, chokes, terminal blocks, some dials, recessed panels, etc. After cutting, a flat file may be used to smooth the rectangular hole.

Small rectangular, screw-type punches, similar to the round ones illustrated in Fig. 207, also are available. While these punches cut relatively small holes, larger holes can be cut with them by making a series of small-area cutouts.

Burr removal

Burrs may be removed from drilled holes by lightly drilling

over them with a drill two sizes larger. Take care to cut only the burr and not enlarge the hole. Larger holes require the use of a knife, scraper or file to cut away protruding burrs and teeth.

Mounting and bolting

All components must be secured solidly to the chassis and panel. If they are not tightly fastened, their subsequent movement in relation to each other can cause faulty electrical operation.

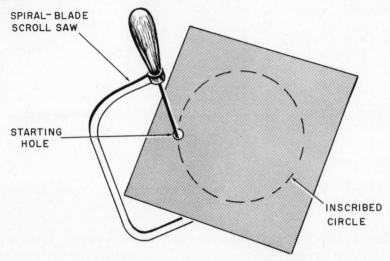

SPIRAL-BLADE
SCROLL SAW

STARTING
HOLE

INSCRIBED
CIRCLE

Fig. 209. *Using coping saw to cut large holes.*

Mounting requirements may be met fairly simply when a wooden breadboard type of construction is employed since the

Table D—SCREW-CLEARANCE HOLES

Screw Size	Number of Drill for Clearance Hole
2–56	43
3–48	39
4–36	33
4–40	33
6–32	28
8–32	18
10–24	11
10–32	10

parts are fastened to the board with wood screws. When using metal chassis and panel, however, machine screws must be used with nuts.

When building equipment in its final form use a lockwasher with each screw to provide an additional safeguard against loosening. (See Fig. 210.) Each clearance hole should be large enough

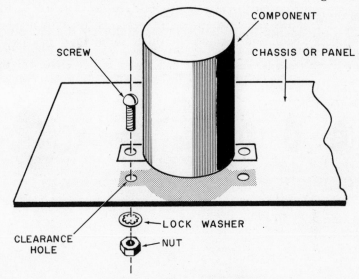

Fig. 210. *Mounting components.*

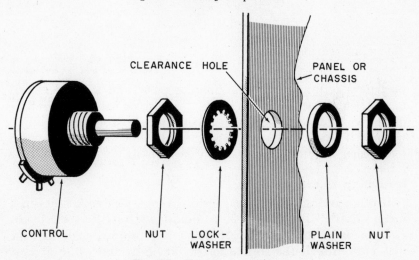

Fig. 211. *Mounting controls.*

for easy insertion and removal of the screw but not so large that the screw can shake around. Table D lists suitable clearance-hole sizes for the machine screws commonly used in electronic construction.

Fig. 211 shows the similar use of nuts, lockwashers and plain washers in mounting controls (rheostats and potentiometers) and switches. Controls, rotary switches and pilot light assemblies usually require ⅜-inch clearance holes; toggle switches ½ inch.

Fig. 212 shows how two insulated washers (usually made of bakelite or fiber), one flat and the other shouldered, are used to

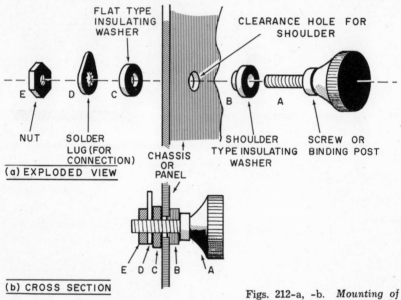

Figs. 212-a, -b. *Mounting of insulated screws or terminals.*

insulate a terminal screw or binding post from a metal chassis or panel on which it is mounted. The size of the clearance hole must give a reasonably snug fit around the shoulder of the upper washer. The solder lug has a toothed clearance hole which gives lockwasher action when the nut is tightened.

Insulating clearance holes

It often is desirable to pass leads through clearance holes in a metal chassis. The power cord almost always enters electronic equipment in this fashion. If the hole is unprotected, its edge may cut through the insulation of the leads and cause a short circuit. This can be prevented by lining the hole with a rubber grommet, as shown in Fig. 213.

Rubber grommets are flexible and are obtainable in a number of sizes to accommodate from one to many leads. The clearance hole is drilled slightly larger than the outside diameter of the neck of the grommet, and the grommet is pressed into place so that its flanges rest on opposite faces of the chassis.

Grounding

Various portions of a circuit often must be "grounded" by connecting them directly to the metal chassis or panel. For this purpose, a solder lug may be bolted to the chassis, as shown in Fig. 214.

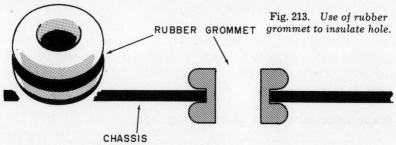

RUBBER GROMMET

Fig. 213. *Use of rubber grommet to insulate hole.*

CHASSIS

An area not less than ¼ inch in diameter around the clearance hole for the lug screw must be cleaned completely (before the lug is installed) of all paint, rust or other material which might prevent good electrical contact. A lockwasher should be used be-

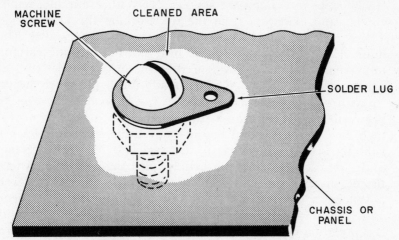

MACHINE SCREW

CLEANED AREA

SOLDER LUG

CHASSIS OR PANEL

Fig. 214. *Attachment of grounding lug.*

tween the nut and the bottom of the chassis or panel, as previously shown in Fig. 210. The screw must be tightened completely in order that the ground connection will be permanently effective.

In metal chassis and panel construction, the panel and chassis must be in good electrical contact with each other; to insure good over-all grounding. To obtain this contact, their touching surfaces must be scraped clean of any paint or rust before the two are fastened together. The fastening should be tight. Failure to observe this rule not only results in poor shielding and poor conduction but has been known to result in electric shock on touching the panel.

Soldering

With very few exceptions, the connections in electronic wiring are soldered. This yields a good, low-resistance electrical bond which is protected mechanically against loosening. A poorly soldered joint can be the source of much trouble, however, hence the electronic technician must master the art of good soldering early in his career.

Preparation and care of soldering iron

To do good work, the soldering iron must be cleaned and tinned at all times. Most modern soldering-iron tips are supplied pre-tinned. But since a few are not and because overheating can destroy the tinned coat, a few remarks regarding tinning are in order.

The steps in tinning are simple: (1) With a fine file, remove all slag and oxidation from the tip, working the faces smooth. The copper tip should have a shiny, smooth appearance when finished. (2) Allow the iron to heat slowly, watching carefully to prevent overheating (evidenced by the bright copper tip turning brownish in color). (3) Frequently touch the slowly heating tip with a piece of rosin-core solder. Just as soon as the iron first begins to melt solder into a pasty mass, allow a little to melt on each face of the tip and spread it over the surface quickly by rubbing briskly with a clean, dry rag. (4) Melt a little more solder on each face and rub briskly until the tip has a uniform, bright, silvery color. The iron now is tinned and ready for work.

Whenever the iron is in use, its tip should be wiped frequently with a clean rag. This will preserve the tinning by preventing the accumulation of oxides. Overheating at any time will burn away the tinned surface, necessitating rescraping and retinning.

The tip of a soldering gun is pre-tinned before sale and, during its useful life, needs only to be wiped regularly with a dry rag while hot.

It is wise to keep on hand at least one new tip for a soldering iron and at least two tips for a soldering gun.

Preparation and soldering of joints

A basic rule among good workmen is that a connection must be mechanically tight before it is soldered. Do not depend upon the solder to fasten the joint together, but make a good mechanical bond and then solder it. This can be done by crimping or splicing leads together and by crimping or tying leads to lugs.

Both parts of the joint must be scrupulously clean before attempting to solder. If they are not, the solder will not "take." Solder runs off greasy metal readily. If a joint is partially clean, the solder will stick only to the clean portions, resulting in a poor joint. A porous ("cold") soldered joint is inefficient both electrically and mechanically. For cleaning, use sandpaper or a knife to remove all enamel or other insulation, dirt and grease from the metal surfaces which are to be soldered. Blow away any dust residue remaining after the cleaning.

Solder ordinarily will not take by itself. A flux is needed. This is obtained easily by using rosin-core solder. The rosin melts ahead of the solder and fluxes the joint. There also are liquid and paste fluxes which may be applied to the metal prior to soldering, and there is acid-core solder. But rosin is a safe flux for electrical work because it does not corrode the joints. This is the only flux we recommend for electronic wiring.

Making the soldered connection

(1) Hold the hot tip of the iron in close contact with the cleaned joint to be soldered. The purpose of this step is to heat the joint thoroughly so that it subsequently will melt the solder. Many workers make the mistake of heating the solder instead of the joint! There is no reason to touch the solder to the iron. (2) When the joint is hot, continue to hold the iron in contact with it and touch the tip of a piece of rosin-core solder to the joint. If the joint is hot enough, the solder will melt and flow like water into all of the crevices of the joint and over it. (3) Remove the iron and allow the joint to cool before disturbing it.

It is good workmanship to use the minimum amount of solder necessary to secure a good joint. There are reasons other than economy for this practice. Large globs of solder enclosing a joint serve no useful purpose and in some high-frequency circuits actually can cause mischief.

Radio hookup wire, used in virtually all electronic wiring, is supplied pre-tinned. Therefore it will solder easily without further treatment. Bare copper wire, on the other hand, must be cleaned brightly and then tinned by coating it with a light film of solder.

When using a soldering gun, release the trigger as soon as the soldering operation has been completed. This allows the gun to cool between operations, preserving its recommended "duty cycle."

Crystal diodes and transistors can be damaged by the heat of soldering. When their pigtail leads must be soldered into a circuit, each lead should be grasped firmly with long-nose pliers. The plier tips should be close to the body of the diode or transistor; that is, between the body and the soldering iron. The large metallic mass of the pliers serves to conduct heat away from the component, preventing its entry inside where it could do damage. Continue to hold the lead with the pliers until there is no doubt that the joint has cooled completely.

Wiring practice

Wiring is the connecting of components together so that they may function properly in conjunction with each other in the circuit. It has been called the principal job in electronic fabrication, mechanical assembly being regarded by some authorities as

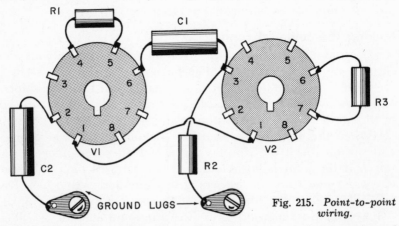

Fig. 215. *Point-to-point wiring.*

essentially nonelectronic. Basically, the wiring process consists of connecting a conductor or component to two or more points, almost always by soldering.

Flexible or semiflexible insulated "hookup" wire is employed principally in electronic wiring. Bare wire is used only when there is no possibility of short circuit or grounding because of the lack of insulation.

34

Two methods of wiring are employed in electronics. The first and simplest is illustrated in Fig. 215 and takes its name, point-to-point, from the fact that leads or components are connected directly between terminal points on other components. Thus, capacitor C1 is connected from terminal 6 of tube socket V1 to terminal 3 of socket V2, no wire being used. Similarly, resistor R2 is connected directly from terminal 3 of socket V2 to the chassis ground lug, and resistor R1 from terminal 4 to terminal 5 of socket V1. A lead from terminal 1 of socket V1 to terminal 1 of socket V2 connects these two points together.

Point-to-point wiring has the advantages of simplicity and directness. It also minimizes undesirable interaction between circuit components (since the latter need not be mounted side by side) and permits leads to be run directly via short routes. It is economical of wire since many of the connections may be completed with the leads of components, as shown in Fig. 215. These leads also hold the components in place. Point-to-point wiring is not always neat, however, and unless care is taken to position components in straight lines a disorderly appearance might result.

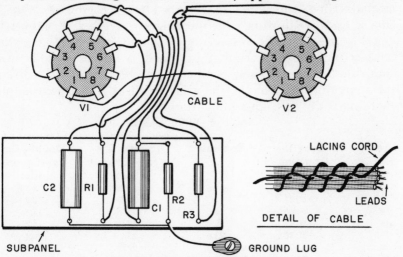

Fig. 216. *Laced and cabled wiring.*

The second method is illustrated in Fig. 216. In this scheme, all of the sundry components are mounted on a single subpanel and leads are run between this panel and such components as tube sockets, transformers, etc. through a single cable. Fig. 216 illustrates how the same circuit shown wired point-to-point in Fig. 215 might appear with cabled wiring. Fig. 216 also shows a

35

detail of the cable, illustrating the bundling of the leads together and tying them with lacing cord.

Cabled wiring is neat and orderly. It allows small parts, like capacitors and resistors, to be grouped together on convenient panels where they are easily accessible for testing and replacement. This type of wiring has the disadvantage that interaction can take place between wires running in the same cable. Some of these leads must be shielded, while others must be grouped in separate cables to prevent stray coupling. It is easily seen, then, that the successful application of this method often requires considerable study as to possible coupling between leads and occasionally much cut-and-try effort after the initial cabling has been completed.

In all wiring operations, the rules of good soldering practice must be observed. Before soldering, strip the insulation from the ends of the hookup wire (or scrape the enamel from enameled wire) for a distance of at least $\frac{1}{4}$ inch. This will allow sufficient exposed wire for making a well-anchored joint before soldering.

Keep all power-line-frequency ac leads close to the chassis. This includes tube-filament leads as well as 115-volt conductors. Where the ac leads are in pairs, twist them tightly together. Leads carrying high-frequency ac (especially rf) should be kept clear of the chassis and should be run in as straight a line as possible. Do not run an ac lead closely parallel to any high-sensitivity portion of a circuit (for example, the grid circuit of a high-gain amplifier) since this will give hum trouble.

Table E—WIRE TABLE

Size	Bare Diameter (mils)	turns-per-linear-inch (close wound coil)		
		Enameled	Single Cotton-Covered (scc)	Double Cotton-Covered (dcc)
10	101.9	9.6	9.25	8.85
12	80.81	12	11.5	10.9
14	64.08	15	14.3	13.5
16	50.82	18.9	17.9	16.7
18	40.30	23.6	22.2	20.4
20	31.96	29.4	27	24.4
22	25.35	37	33.9	30
24	20.10	46.3	41.5	35.6
26	15.94	58	50.2	41.8
28	12.64	72.7	60.2	48.6
30	10.03	90.5	71.4	55.6
32	7.95	113	83.4	62.9
34	6.30	143	97.1	70
36	5.00	175	111	77
38	3.96	224	125	83.3
40	3.14	282	141	90.9

Coil winding

Many of the coils used in experimental electronic equipment may be purchased ready-made. Others must be wound by the technician.

Except in rare instances, coils to be made by the experimenter are of the single-layer type. They are either wound on cylindrical plastic forms or are air-wound. By air-wound is meant that no supporting form or tube is used but the turns of wire are self-supporting. A single-layer coil may be close-wound (meaning that each turn is laid close against the previous one) or space-wound (meaning that each turn is separated from the other by some amount). In a space-wound coil, the distance from the first turn to the last one is specified as the winding length. Only insulated wire may be used in winding a close-wound coil, otherwise successive turns will short-circuit. Enameled wire generally is used, but single cotton-covered (scc), double cotton-covered (dcc), and double silk-covered (dsc) sometimes are specified.

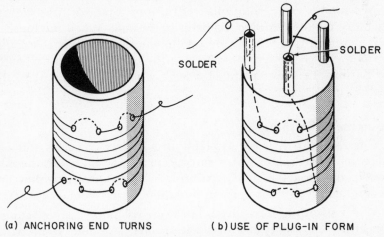

(a) ANCHORING END TURNS   (b) USE OF PLUG-IN FORM

Figs. 217-a, -b. *Coil-winding techniques.*

Wire is specified by number according to the B & S (Brown and Sharpe) gauge. This number is closely associated with the diameter of the wire. For example, No. 18 bare wire is 40.3 mils in diameter, (1 mil = 1/1,000 of an inch). The larger the wire number, the smaller it is in diameter. Thus, No. 40 is only about 3 mils diameter. Table E lists the sizes of copper wire (and various types of insulation) commonly employed in electronic work, together with the number of turns-per-inch each would give in a close-wound coil.

Fig. 217-a shows how the end turns of a coil wound on a form can be anchored to prevent the coil from slipping off the ends of the tube. Several close-spaced pairs of small holes are drilled as shown and the end turns threaded in and out of them. Fig. 217-b shows how a coil is wound on a plug-in form. After winding in the same manner shown in the previous illustration, the ends of the leads are cleaned of insulation and tinned. Then they are pulled through two of the base pins, as shown, and secured by melting solder into the hollow pins. Do this by heating the pin with the soldering iron and then holding rosin-core solder at the open end of the pin until the solder melts and runs in. When the joint has cooled, the excess wire is clipped off and the soldered end of the pin filed or scraped smooth.

A finished coil may be given one or more coats of coil dope or collodion to cement the turns in place.

Air-wound coils are made with heavier wire (No. 20 and lower) to obtain rigidity. The best way to make this type of coil is to close-wind the required number of turns on a pipe or tube slightly smaller than the required diameter of the coil. When the finished coil is released, it will spring out to the desired diameter. The turns then may be separated to give the required winding length by passing the blunt point of a lead pencil around between the turns.

Equipment finishing

Chassis and panels are available in a variety of colors and finishes including plain, satin finish, crackle, wrinkle, leatherette and hammertone. Usually, painting is not required unless the experimenter fabricates his foundation units from raw metal.

When painting is required, however, several types of lacquer, for brush and spray-gun application, are available from paint dealers and radio supply houses. Wrinkle and crackle finishes are obtainable in addition to plain lacquers. Best results usually are obtained by baking the enamel or lacquer although simple air-dried finishes are satisfactory when the painted object will not be subject to mechanical abuse.

A full complement of inexpensive decals for labeling electronic instruments is available in books. These labels are cut from the pages, soaked in water and transferred to the panel or chassis. Decals are obtainable in white, black or bronzes and impart a professional appearance to finished apparatus.

Color codes

Color markings (dots or rings) on electronic components indicate their values and ratings. Fig. 218 shows the color codes used in marking resistors.

Typical examples

Insulated axial-lead resistor. Refer to Fig. 218-a. The first ring color indicates the first figure in the ohmage rating, the second ring the second figure, the third ring the number of ciphers following the second figure and the fourth ring the resistance tolerance. Thus, a resistor marked with successive red, yellow, orange and gold bands (reading from left to right) would have the following value: 2 (red) 4 (yellow) plus 3 (orange) ciphers = 24,000 ohms. The final gold band indicates a tolerance of 5%.

Radial-lead dot resistor. See Fig. 218-b. The body color of the resistor indicates the first figure in the resistance rating; the

RESISTORS

(a) INSULATED UNINSULATED	FIRST RING BODY COLOR	SECOND RING END COLOR	THIRD RING DOT COLOR
COLOR	1ST FIGURE	2ND FIGURE	MULTIPLIER
BLACK	0	0	NONE
BROWN	1	1	0
RED	2	2	00
ORANGE	3	3	,000
YELLOW	4	4	0,000
GREEN	5	5	00,000
BLUE	6	6	000,000
VIOLET	7	7	0,000,000
GRAY	8	8	00,000,000
WHITE	9	9	000,000,000
GOLD		0.1	
SILVER		0.01	

TOLERANCE: GOLD 5%, SILVER 10%, NONE 20%

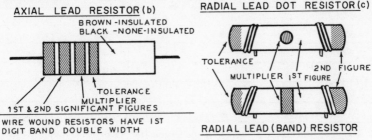

AXIAL LEAD RESISTOR (b)

BROWN -INSULATED
BLACK -NONE-INSULATED

TOLERANCE
MULTIPLIER
1ST & 2ND SIGNIFICANT FIGURES

WIRE WOUND RESISTORS HAVE 1ST DIGIT BAND DOUBLE WIDTH

RADIAL LEAD DOT RESISTOR (c)

TOLERANCE
MULTIPLIER 1ST FIGURE 2ND FIGURE

RADIAL LEAD (BAND) RESISTOR

Fig. 218. *Resistor color code and methods of coding resistors.*

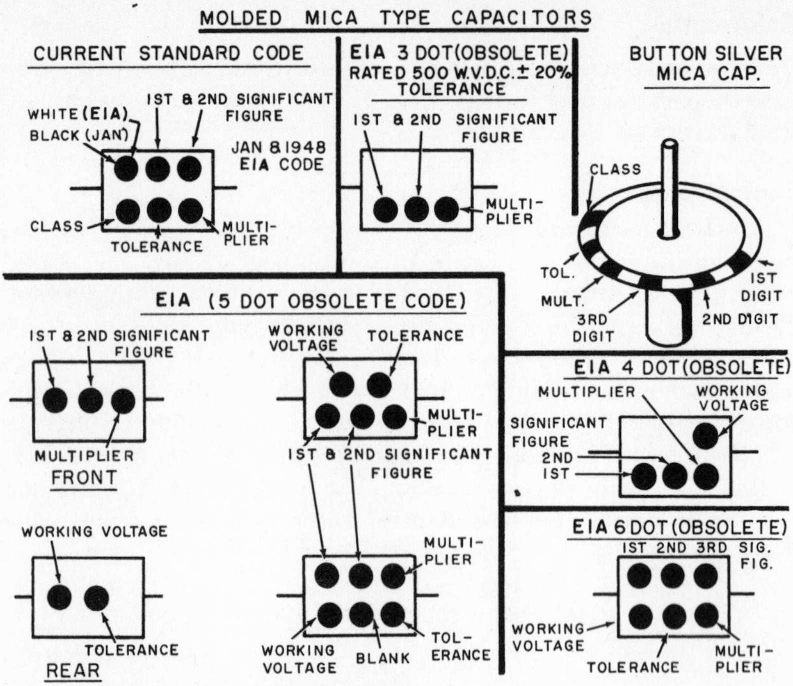

MOLDED MICA TYPE CAPACITORS

Fig. 219. *Mica and molded-paper capacitor color codes and methods of coding molded-mica type capacitors.*

FOR MICA AND MOLDED PAPER

COLOR	SIGNIFICANT FIGURE, OR NO. OF ZEROS, OR DECIMAL MULTIPLIER	VDCW	TOLERANCE
BLACK	0	—	—
BROWN	1	100	1%
RED	2	200	2%
ORANGE	3	300	3%
YELLOW	4	400	4%
GREEN	5	500	5%
BLUE	6	600	—
VIOLET	7	700	—
GRAY	8	800	—
WHITE	9	900	—
GOLD	—	1000	—
SILVER	—	2000	—
NONE	—	500	—

CERAMIC CAPACITORS

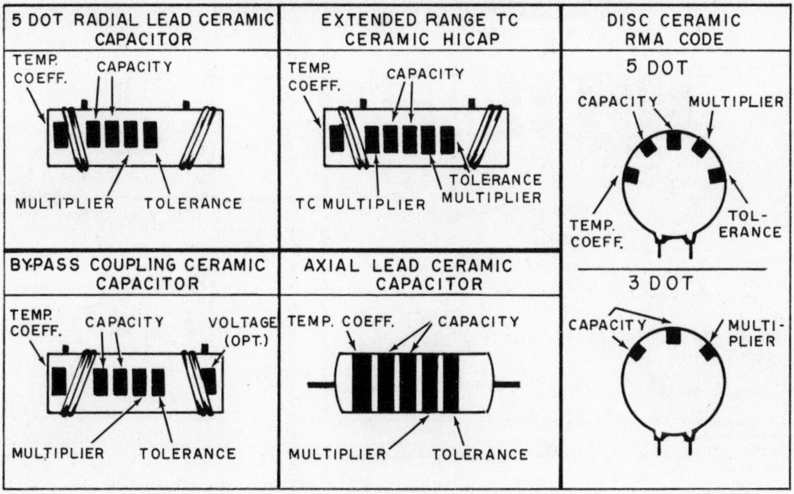

5 DOT RADIAL LEAD CERAMIC CAPACITOR	EXTENDED RANGE TC CERAMIC HICAP	DISC CERAMIC RMA CODE
TEMP. COEFF. CAPACITY MULTIPLIER TOLERANCE	TEMP. COEFF. CAPACITY TOLERANCE MULTIPLIER TC MULTIPLIER	5 DOT CAPACITY MULTIPLIER TEMP. COEFF. TOL-ERANCE
BYPASS COUPLING CERAMIC CAPACITOR	**AXIAL LEAD CERAMIC CAPACITOR**	3 DOT
TEMP. COEFF. CAPACITY VOLTAGE (OPT.) MULTIPLIER TOLERANCE	TEMP. COEFF. CAPACITY MULTIPLIER TOLERANCE	CAPACITY MULTI-PLIER

CERAMICS

COLOR	SIGNIFICANT FIGURE	DECIMAL MULTIPLIER	CAPACITOR TOLERANCE	TEMP. COEFF. PPM/°C
BLACK	0	1	± 20%	0
BROWN	1	10	±1%	−30
RED	2	100	±2%	−80
ORANGE	3	1000		−150
YELLOW	4			−220
GREEN	5		±5%	−330
BLUE	6			−470
VIOLET	7			−750
GRAY	8	0.01		30
WHITE	9	0.1		500

Fig. 220. *Ceramic capacitor color code and methods of coding ceramic capacitors.*

color of the right end of the resistor the second figure; the center dot the number of ciphers following the second figure and the color of the left end the resistance tolerance. Thus, a green-bodied resistor with violet right end, silver left end and red dot has the value: 5 (green) 7 (violet) plus 2 ciphers = 5,700 ohms. The silver left-end color means a resistance tolerance of 10%.

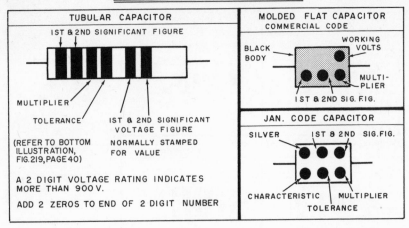

Fig. 221. *Methods of coding molded-paper type capacitors.*

Molded mica capacitor. See Fig. 219. With the existing standard code, the first dot (reading from left to right) in the top row indicates whether the capacitor is RETMA[1] (Radio-Electronics-Television Manufacturers Association) or JAN (Joint Army-Navy), the next dot color the first significant figure, the right-most dot the second figure; the right-most dot in the bottom row the multiplier and the lower center dot the capacitance tolerance. Thus, a color scheme of top row (left to right) of white, red, green; bottom row (right to left) of brown, green, blank indicates a RETMA (white) capacitor with the capacitance of 2 (red) 5 (green) times 1 (brown) = 25 $\mu\mu$f. The lower center green (5) dot indicates a capacitance tolerance of 5%.

Axial-lead ceramic capacitor. See Fig. 220. The first (left-most) color band indicates the temperature coefficient, the second band the first figure of the capacitance, third band second figure of capacitance, fourth band decimal multiplier for capacitance and fifth band the capacitance tolerance. Thus, an axial-lead ceramic capacitor reading (left to right) black, brown, green, brown, white is identified as follows: zero (black) temperature coefficient. Capacitance of 1 (brown) 5 (green) times 10 (brown) = 15 × 10 = 150 $\mu\mu$f. The right-most white band shows that the capacitance tolerance is 10%.

Molded paper type capacitor. Fig. 221 shows methods of coding molded-paper type capacitors.

---

[1] Now known as Electronic Industries Association (EIA).

amplifiers

AMPLIFIERS perform some of the most essential electronic functions. Many electronic circuits basically are amplifiers although their end applications may be for purposes which on the surface do not appear to be amplification. For example, some special amplifier circuits make calculations, others measure elec-

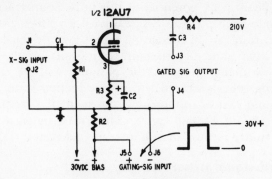

SIMPLE GATED AMPLIFIER (Fig. 301)

Resistors: R1, R2—470,000 ohms; R3—3,300 ohms; R4—100,000 ohms

Capacitors: C1—.01-μf 400-volt tubular; C2 —10-μf 50-volt electrolytic; C3—.1-μf 400-volt tubular

Tube: 12AU7
Socket: 9-pin miniature
Miscellaneous: J1, J2, J3, J4, J5, J6—terminal connectors

Fig. 301. *Triode amplifier used as an electronic switch.*

tricity and still others permit the control of objects at a distance. Such is the domain of the amplifier.

This chapter does not attempt to cover the entire broad field of amplifiers. Instead, it presents a number of practical circuits which will be useful to the experimenter. These circuits may be used alone or in conjunction with other circuits. They are fundamental building blocks.

Simple gated amplifier

Occcasional experimental applications call for a simple amplifier capable of being switched repetitively on and off electronically at high speeds. Such amplifiers are the basis of the electronic switch which enables several signals to be displayed simultaneously on an oscilloscope screen. They are used also in digital computers, electronic counters and in some radar circuits.

Fig. 301 shows the circuit of a simple gated amplifier of this type.[1] The signal (X-signal) under observation or to be switched is applied to the grid of the triode through capacitor C1. The gating or switching signal consists of positive square or rectangular pulses having 30 volts peak amplitude. These pulses are developed across resistor R2.

During the intervals when the gating signal is zero, the tube is cut off by the 30-volt negative dc bias and no signal appears at the OUTPUT terminals. During the positive interval of the gating pulse, the 30-volt peak potential of this pulse counteracts the bias and the triode transmits the X-signal with a voltage gain of 11.4.

The repetition rate of the gating signal may be selected to suit individual conditions. The length (duration) of the pulse determines how many cycles of the X-signal will be transmitted each time the tube is switched to its conducting state. For common electronic switch applications, the switching frequency may be between 10 and 100,000 cycles. The gating signal may be supplied by a multivibrator or square-wave generator.

Ac-operated signal tracer

Fig. 302 is the complete circuit diagram of an af-rf signal tracer.

---

[1] All resistors (in all circuits) are $\frac{1}{2}$ watt unless otherwise specified. Chassis and panel descriptions are not included since this is a matter of personal choice. Miscellaneous hardware, wire, phone jacks, plugs, etc. are not described since these are available in a large variety and also are a matter of personal choice.

Tube filaments are not shown unless the filament hookup is, in some way, unusual.

The circuits are shown leading to a source of B+ voltage but the power supplies delivering the B+ are not included with the circuits. To do so would involve needless repetition. Before building the circuits, it would be well to start with a power supply of the type shown in Fig. 501. A variable-voltage power supply—preferably one that can also deliver 6.3 and 12.6 volts ac for filament power—is a necessity for the serious-minded experimenter.

This specialized high-gain amplifier is widely employed for dynamic troubleshooting in radio, television and electronic equipment. Both visual (electron-eye tube) and aural (loudspeaker) output indications are provided.

In af signal tracing, the signal is applied to the AUDIO INPUT

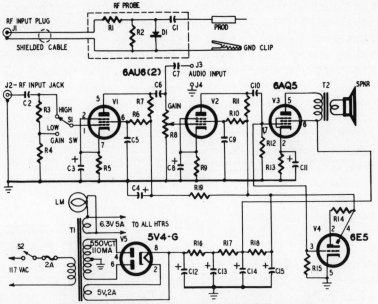

AC-OPERATED AF–RF SIGNAL-TRACING AMPLIFIER (Fig. 302)

Resistors: R1—10,000 ohms; R2, R3, R6, R10, R14, R15—1 megohm; R4—100.000 ohms; R5, R9—1,000 ohms; R7, R11—220,000 ohms; R8—500,000-ohm pot; R12—470,000 ohms; R13—390 ohms, 1 watt; R16—1,000 ohms, 10 watts; R17—5,000 ohms, 5 watts; R18—25,000 ohms, 25 watts; R19—1,000 ohms, 2 watts

Capacitors: C1—.01-μf 500-volt mica; C2, C5, C7, C9—.1-μf 400-volt tubular; C3, C8—10-μf 25-volt electrolytic; C4—8-μf 450-volt electrolytic; C6, C10—.02-μf 400-volt tubular; C11—20-μf 25-volt electrolytic; C12, C13—dual 20-μf 450-volt electrolytic; C14, C15—dual 20-μf 450-volt electrolytic

Transformers: T1—Triad R-12B or equivalent; T2—Triad S-29X or equivalent

Tubes: V1, V2—6AU6; V3—6AQ5; V4—6E5; V5—5V4-G; D1—1N34 crystal diode

Sockets: 7-pin miniature (3); octal; 6-pin

Miscellaneous: S1—spdt switch; S2—spst; J1—phone plug; J2—phone jack; J3, J4—terminal connectors; 2-amp fuse; LM—No. 47 pilot-lamp assembly; probe housing; test prod; alligator clip

Fig. 302. *Signal tracer can be used for servicing radio and television receivers.*

terminals and only the last two stages of the amplifier are used. The crystal diode type rf probe is used in rf signal tracing. The diode circuit demodulates an AM signal and applies the resulting audio frequency voltage to the input grid of the first 6AU6 amplifier stage.

The input signal (af or rf) causes the electron-eye tube shadow to close and also produces a loudspeaker signal. The gain-control potentiometer is adjusted to accommodate various signal levels. Signal strength can be estimated by observing the amount of eye closure and the volume of the speaker signal. In addition to the smooth variation of the gain control, a two-position gain switch is provided at the input of the amplifier. An rf attenuation of approximately 10 to 1 is obtained when this switch is in its LOW position.

With the rf probe plugged into the amplifier, an amplitude-modulated test signal may be traced through a superheterodyne receiver from the antenna terminal to the second detector input. From the second detector output to the loudspeaker voice coil, a

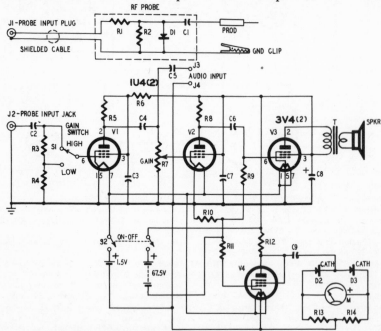

BATTERY-OPERATED AF–RF SIGNAL-TRACING AMPLIFIER (Fig. 303)

Resistors: R1—10,000 ohms; R2, R3—1 megohm; R4, R5, R6, R8—100,000 ohms; R7 —3.3 megohms; R9, R11—470,000 ohms; R10—470 ohms; R12—3,300 ohms, 1 watt; R13, R14—100 ohms

Capacitors: C1—.1-μf 500-volt mica; C2, C3, C5, C7—.1-μf 400-volt tubular; C4, C6— .02-μf 400-volt tubular; C8—10-μf 150-volt electrolytic; C9—1-μf 400-volt tubular

Transformer: T—output (Stancor A-3856 or equivalent)
Tubes: V1, V2—1U4; V3, V4—3V4; D1, D2, D3—1N34 crystal diode
Sockets: 7-pin miniature (4)
Miscellaneous: S1—spdt switch; S2—dpdt; M—0-1-ma dc meter; J1—phone plug; J2— phone jack; J3, J4—terminal connectors; probe housing; test prod; alligator clip; 1½-volt battery; 67½-volt battery

Fig. 303. *Battery-operated signal tracer is independent of the power line.*

simple shielded test probe connected to the AUDIO INPUT terminals will permit audio tracing. Similarly, the AUDIO INPUT of the signal tracer may be used in tracing a test signal throughout an audio amplifier or audio system.

The self-contained power supply uses small-sized components and can be made compact. The entire signal-tracing amplifier thus is self-contained and power-line-operated.

Battery-operated signal tracer

When complete isolation from the power line is required or when troubleshooting at locations remote from power outlets, a battery-operated signal tracer is invaluable.

Fig. 303 is the circuit of a high-gain signal-tracing amplifier operating on the same principle as the ac-operated instrument described in the foregoing section. Since battery-operated electron-eye tubes are not available, a meter type visual indicator is employed. A loudspeaker provides aural signals.

The battery-operated signal tracer has the same general configuration and is operated in the same manner as the ac unit, except that input signals produce a meter deflection. This deflection is proportional to the signal strength. A smooth gain control and a two-step gain switch are provided.

Battery drain with small portable batteries is low enough to insure good life, provided the instrument is switched off whenever it is not being used.

Hearing aid

Fig. 304 is the circuit of a small-sized hearing aid which may be built with readily available components.

The three-stage high-gain amplifier employs Raytheon transistors. A type 2N133 low-noise transistor is used in the input stage. Type CK721 transistors are used in the intermediate and output stages. For highest power gain, transformer coupling is employed between stages. The low-impedance microphone (M) and the earpiece (P) are connected directly to the input and output transistors, respectively.

A penlight cell or a longer-life mercury cell (such as Mallory RM1R) is used as the single battery. Good battery life is obtained with this amplifier.

An entire, ready-made, subminiature transistor amplifier (Centralab type TA-11) also may be employed in this hearing aid to reduce wiring labor and to simplify mechanical construction.

This amplifier is only 1.175 inches long, 0.665 inch wide and 0.250 inch thick. It is hermetically sealed and the only external connections required are those to the battery, microphone, ear-

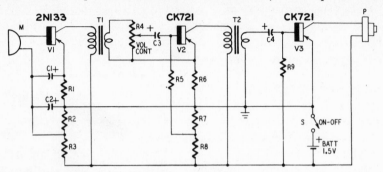

HEARING AID (Fig. 304)

Resistors: R1, R6—820 ohms; R2, R5, R7—4,700 ohms; R3, R8—10,000 ohms; R4—10,000-ohm miniature pot; R9—2.7 megohms

Capacitors: C1, C2, C3, C4—1-μf miniature electrolytic

Transformers: T1, T2—20,000-ohm primary; 1,000-ohm secondary (Argonne AR-104)

Transistors: V1—2N133; V2, V3—CK721

Sockets: Transistor (3)

Miscellaneous: S—spst switch (on volume control) P—magnetic earpiece (Lafayette MS-260); M—1-inch magnetic mike (Shure MC-10A); 1½-volt battery

Fig. 304. *Hearing aid is a high-gain three-stage audio amplifier.*

piece, volume control and ON–OFF switch. It employs four low-noise transistors in an R-C-coupled circuit.

The hearing aid may be employed also as a sound-survey device, stethoscope, rumble detector or sounding device.

Microphone-handle preamplifier

The small size of a high-gain junction-transistor amplifier operated from a single 1-½-volt miniature cell enables the mounting of such an amplifier completely inside the handle or case of a microphone. In this way, a high-quality microphone (such as a dynamic) having low-voltage output can be utilized in applications (such as mobile-radio transmission) where the required higher signal voltage is supplied by the transistor circuit.

Fig. 305 shows the circuit of the transistor preamplifier. A low-noise type of transistor (2N133) is used. Low-noise operation is important for minimizing hiss when using a transistor preamplifier ahead of a high-gain main amplifier.

The tiny output transformer is a UTC type SSO-3. Transformer coupling into a low-impedance line is recommended for reduction of interference pickup. However, R-C output coupling may be used if necessary. Replace the primary of the output transformer with a 22,000-ohm, ½-watt resistor, and couple the collector to the output line through a 1-μf miniature tantalum electrolytic capacitor. R-C coupling of this type must feed into

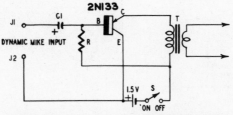

MICROPHONE-HANDLE PREAMPLIFIER (Fig. 305)

Resistor: R—100,000 ohms

Capacitor: C1—1-μf miniature electrolytic

Transformer: T—UTC SSO-3 or equivalent

Transistor: 2N133 (Raytheon)
Socket: Transistor
Miscellaneous: S—spst switch; J1, J2—terminal connectors; 1½-volt battery

Fig. 305. *This amplifier is small enough to be built inside the handle of a microphone.*

the high-impedance grid-ground circuit of the main amplifier. Voltage gain of the preamplifier when operated into such high impedance is approximately 90.

The ON-OFF switch can be a microphone-handle handgrip switch. Current drain from the 1-1½-volt cell is 20 to 25 micro-amperes. This small current insures long life with a penlight cell.

Wide-band instrument amplifier

Fig. 306 shows a wide-band video type amplifier suitable for boosting signal voltages before applying them to an oscilloscope or ac vacuum-tube voltmeter. This amplifier is also usable for raising the output level of signal generators. A maximum voltage gain of approximately 100 is obtained when the amplifier works into a load resistance of 0.5 megohm or higher. Frequency response is flat within ± 1-½ db from 60 cycles to 2 mc. As a wide-range preamplifier, this circuit will improve the sensitivity of an oscilloscope vertical amplifier and will convert an ac vtvm into a millivoltmeter.

Winding specifications for the peaking coils (L1, L2 and L3) are given in the parts list for Fig. 306. Coil L1 is 25, L2 is 72, and L3 is 48 microhenries. If the reader does not care to wind those coils, commercial slug-tuned inductors may be used. For example, L1 may be a Miller No. 4508, L2 Miller No. 4511 and L3 Miller No. 4509.

Gain-control potentiometer R1 is placed at the input of the amplifier. This component provides the smooth, continuous control of gain which is suitable for most purposes. In accurate instrumentation, however, a step-type attenuator is more desirable.

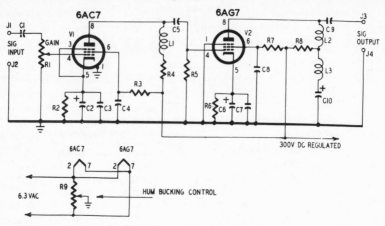

WIDE-BAND INSTRUMENT AMPLIFIER (Fig. 306)

Resistors: R1—1-megohm pot; R2—150 ohms, 1 watt; R3—62,000 ohms, 1 watt; R4—1,300 ohms, 1 watt; R5—270,000 ohms; R6—68-ohms, 2-watt wirewound; R7—27,000 ohms; R8—3,500 ohms, 10 watts; R9—100-ohm wirewound pot
Capacitors: C1—.1-μf 400-volt tubular (see text); C2, C6—10-μf 25-volt electrolytic; C3, C4, C5, C7, C8, C9—.1-μf 600-volt tubular; C10—8-μf 600-volt electrolytic

Coils: L1—50 turns No. 24 enameled wire closewound on ¾-inch-diameter form; L2—84 turns No. 30 enameled wire on ¾-inch-diameter form, spaced to 1 inch; L3—69 turns No. 30 enameled wire on ¾-inch-diameter form, spaced to 1 inch
Tubes: V1—6AC7; V2—6AG7
Sockets: octal (2)
Miscellaneous: J1, J2, J3, J4—terminal connectors

Fig. 306. *Video amplifier features hum-bucking control.*

The over-all frequency response will be somewhat better when input coupling capacitor C1 is omitted. However, this capacitor must be used for blocking purposes when a dc component is present in the signal under measurement.

The 300-volt dc supply must be well regulated to stabilize the amplifier gain. It also must be well filtered. The ac filament supply presents no difficulty at the low frequencies within the range of the amplifier since potentiometer R9 provides excellent hum bucking.

High-selectivity if amplifier

Fig. 307 shows the circuit of a selective 50-kc amplifier suitable for use in the if amplifier channels of CW radio receivers or test instruments such as heterodyne wave analyzers. At maximum selectivity, 50-db rejection is obtained at points only 200 cycles above and below 50 kc. This amplifier utilizes the Harris Q-multiplier principle involving positive feedback into the tuned circuit to boost Q and selectivity.[2]

Potentiometer R6 controls the amount of positive feedback and, accordingly, the selectivity. The sharpest tuning is obtained at large values of feedback (low-resistance settings of R6). Excessive feedback will cause oscillation.

The single-tuned circuit consists of slug-tuned coil L shunted by the two series-connected capacitors, C5 and C6. The capacitors

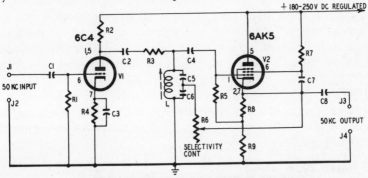

HIGH-SELECTIVITY 50-KC IF AMPLIFIER (Fig. 307)

Resistors: R1—1 megohm; R2—100,000 ohms; R3—2 megohms; R4—5,600 ohms; R5—470,000 ohms; R6—50,000-ohm pot; R7—220,000 ohms; R8—2,200 ohms, 1 watt; R9—62,000 ohms, 1 watt
Capacitors: C1, C2, C4, C7, C8—.01-μf 500-volt mica; C3—.25-μf 200-volt tubular; C5,
C6—.008-μf 500-volt mica (see text)
Coil: L—ferrite tuned, 0.5–5 mh (Miller 6313 or equivalent)
Tubes: V1—6C4; V2—6AK5
Sockets: 7-pin miniature (2)
Miscellaneous: J1, J2, J3, J4—terminal connectors

Fig. 307. *High-selectivity amplifier utilizes positive feedback.*

should be matched within 2%. This matching is more important than the absolute capacitance values since the coil is easily adjusted for 50-kc resonance. With the .008-μf capacitors shown (C5 and C6), L will be adjusted to 2-½ millihenries for 50-kc resonance.

Initial alignment is performed by feeding a 50-kc unmodulated signal from a signal generator or crystal oscillator into the 50-kc input terminals and adjusting L for peak deflection of an rf vacuum-tube voltmeter connected to the 50-kc output terminals. During this adjustment, potentiometer R6 should be set for medium selectivity.

The amplifier gain and selectivity are very sensitive to fluctua-

<hr>

[2] "Simplified Q Multiplier," by H. E. Harris, Electronics; May, 1951; page 130.

tions in the dc supply voltage. The 180-250-volt dc supply must be excellently regulated. A vacuum-tube electronic regulator is preferred to the simple voltage-regulator type circuits. See Fig. 503 in Chapter 5 for a suitable power supply. The power supply may be mounted on the same chassis as the amplifier, provided care is taken in placement to prevent heating of the amplifier components by power supply components.

Bandpass af amplifier

A tuned amplifier which will pass one audio frequency (or a narrow band of frequencies) while discriminating against all frequencies on each side often is required in communications and instrumentation. A familiar instrument application is used as a bridge null detector. Here, the bandpass amplifier discriminates against harmonics, hum and noise and thus sharpens the bridge balance.

The two circuits shown in Figs. 308-a,-b are single-frequency amplifiers designed for 1,000-cycle operation. The operating frequency of these circuits may be shifted, however, by changing the values of certain components.

R-C tuned type

In Fig. 308-a, selectivity is obtained by means of degenerative feedback in the second triode of the 12AX7 through the parallel-T null network (C5, C6, C7, R7, R8 and R9). Degeneration cancels the amplifier gain at all frequencies except the null frequency of this network. At this frequency, the amplifier accordingly passes signals. This accounts for the bandpass action.

The R and C values in the parallel-T network have been chosen for 1,000-cycle operation. Discrimination is 5.5 to 1 at points an octave above and below 1,000 cycles; that is, at 500 and 2,000 cycles. Maximum over-all voltage gain at the pass frequency of 1,000 cycles is 650. The response frequency is $f = 1/6.28R7C5$ where f is in cycles/sec (cps), R in ohms and C in farads. From this relationship, R and C values may be determined for amplifier operation at other frequencies. For any desired frequency, $C = 1/6.28fR$ and $R = 1/6.28fC$. In the network, R7 must equal R8; R9 must be one-half of R7. Also C5 must equal C7, and $C6 = 2C7$.

The R-C tuned amplifier has the advantage of simplicity due to the use of resistors and capacitors only. These components suit the circuit ideally to conditions where the presence of strong magnetic fields might induce hum into inductive components.

L-C tuned type

The 1-octave rejection of approximately 15 db afforded by the R-C tuned bandpass amplifier is insufficient in some instances.

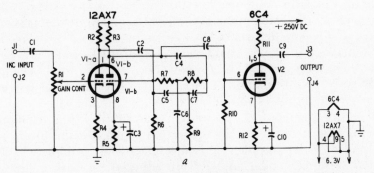

BANDPASS AF AMPLIFIERS (Fig. 308)

(a) Resistance-capacitance tuned type

Resistors: R1—500,000 ohm pot; R2, R3—100,000 ohms; R4—2,200 ohms; R5—1,000 ohms; R6—1 megohm; R7, R8—82,000 ohms, 1 watt, precision; R9—39,000 ohms, 1 watt, precision; R10—470,000 ohms; R11—82,000 ohms; R12—1,500 ohms

Capacitors: C1, C2, C8—.01-μf 400-volt tubu-lar; C3, C10—10-μf 25-volt electrolytic; C4—.02-μf 400-volt tubular; C5, C7—.002-μf 500-volt mica; C6—.004-μf 500-volt mica; C9—.1-μf 400-volt tubular

Tubes: V1—12AX7; V2—6C4

Sockets: 9-pin miniature; 7-pin miniature

Miscellaneous: J1, J2, J3, J4—terminal con-nectors

Fig. 308-a. *Tuned amplifier is designed to pass a single frequency or a narrow band.*

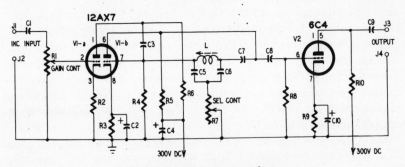

(b) Inductance-capacitance tuned type

Resistors: R1—1-megohm pot; R2—2,200 ohms; R3—1,000 ohms; R4—1 megohm; R5, R6—100,000 ohms; R7—500,000-ohm pot; R8—470,000 ohms; R9—1,500 ohms; R10—82,000 ohms

Capacitors: C1, C9—.1-μf 400-volt tubular; C2, C10—25-μf 50-volt electrolytic; C3, C8—.01-μf 400-volt tubular; C4—10-μf 450-volt electrolytic; C5, C6—.01-μf 500-volt mica; C7—.05-μf 400-volt tubular

Coil: L—tunable 5-h choke (UTC VIC-15 or equivalent)

Tubes: V1—12AX7; V2—6C4

Sockets: 9-pin miniature; 7-pin miniature

Miscellaneous: J1, J2, J3, J4—terminal con-nectors

Fig. 308-b. *Greater selectivity is obtained by using an L-C instead of an R-C arrangement.*

Greatly increased selectivity is afforded by replacing the R-C network with a bridged-T null circuit embodying a high-Q inductor. Such a null circuit is comprised of L, C5, C6 and R7 in Fig. 308-b. With this amplifier, rejection at the 1-octave points is 300 to 1, or 50 db. Maximum over-all voltage gain at the pass frequency, 1,000 cycles, is 300.

Tunable inductor L is assumed to be adjusted exactly to 5 henries. The values of C5 and C6 have been selected for 1,000-cycle resonance with this value of inductance. The setting of potentiometer R7 improves the selectivity of the circuit without influencing its frequency of operation. At a critical setting, it affords the highest resonant rise in the output signal. In the initial adjustment of the amplifier, a 1,000-cycle signal is applied to the INPUT terminals and L and R7 are adjusted for peak deflection of an ac vacuum-tube voltmeter connected to the OUTPUT terminals.

Network values may be selected for amplifier operation at other frequencies. At any frequency, $C5 = C6 = 2/39.5f^2L$ where C is in farads, L in henries and f in cps.

Sharp-response af signal-rejection amplifier

This amplifier circuit (Fig. 309) accomplishes the opposite action of the amplifiers described in the previous section. That is, signal rejection is provided at one frequency (or a very narrow band of frequencies). This rejection principle is utilized in communications and instrumentation to remove an unwanted frequency while passing all other frequencies relatively untouched, such as the 10-kc whistle filter used in some hi-fi AM tuners. A common application is the distortion meter in which the fundamental test frequency is eliminated from a distorted waveform, leaving only the harmonics which then may be totalized by a voltage measurement.

The circuit in Fig. 309 is that of a simple 2-stage R-C-coupled amplifier with a bridged-T null network (L, C6, C7 and R7) inserted between stages. The network, previously described, removes the frequency to which it is responsive and passes all others. The values of the network components have been selected for 1,000-cycle rejection. Inductor L is assumed to be adjusted to 5 henries and is a high-Q component. Adjustment of potentiometer R7 improves the null which becomes complete (zero transmission) at a critical setting of this potentiometer.

Capacitance values for C6 and C7 may be chosen for amplifier operation at other frequencies. At any frequency, $C6 = C7 = 2/39.5f^2L$ where C is in farads, L in henries and f in cps.

Initial adjustment of the circuit is simple: Apply a test signal at the desired frequency from a signal generator connected to the SIGNAL INPUT terminals. Connect an ac vtvm to the SIGNAL

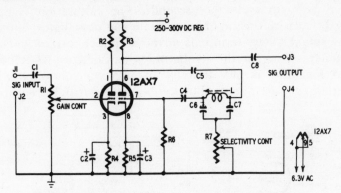

SHARP-RESPONSE SIGNAL-REJECTION AMPLIFIER (Fig. 309)

Resistors: R1—1-megohm pot; R2, R3—100,000 ohms; R4—2,200 ohms; R5—1,000 ohms; R6—1 megohm; R7—500,000-ohm pot

Capacitors: C1, C8—.1-μf 400-volt tubular; C2, C3—25-μf 50-volt electrolytic; C4, C5—.05-μf 400-volt tubular; C6, C7—.01-μf 500-volt mica

Coil: L—tunable 5-h choke (UTC VIC-15 or equivalent)

Tube: 12AX7

Socket: 9-pin miniature

Miscellaneous: J1, J2, J3, J4—terminal connectors

Fig. 309. *This circuit provides rejection at one frequency or a very narrow band of frequencies.*

OUTPUT terminals. Then adjust L and R7 for complete elimination of the signal, as indicated by downward deflection of the meter to zero.

With the components specified in Fig. 309, signal rejection at 1,000 cycles is better than 1,000 to 1, or 60 db.

Tuned af signal-rejection amplifier

When signals of different frequencies must be rejected separately at will, a tunable rejection-type amplifier is advantageous.

Fig. 310 shows a simple amplifier which can be tuned continuously to reject any signal in the range 50 to 10,000 cycles. Rejection is accomplished by means of a Wien bridge null circuit (C6, C7, R6, R7, R8, R9 and R10) inserted between the two amplifier stages.

The tuning control is the 2-gang 0.5-megohm potentiometer (R6-R7). Capacitors C6 and C7 each are made up of .007 and

.0001 μf in parallel. These capacitors must be matched closely. The 1,000-ohm resistance-balance potentiometer (R10) serves to deepen the null. It compensates for differences between R6 and R7. Resistors R8 and R9 must be chosen for exact values.

A dial attached to potentiometer R6-R7 may be graduated to read directly in cycles per second. The calibration is accomplished best with the aid of an accurate audio oscillator connected to the SIGNAL INPUT terminals of the amplifier. At each selected frequency setting of the oscillator, potentiometer R6-R7 is adjusted for null, as indicated by an ac vtvm connected to the SIGNAL OUTPUT terminals. The knob attached to R10 requires no

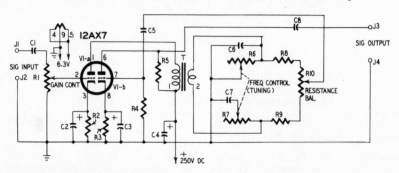

WIDE-BAND TUNED-AF SIGNAL-REJECTION AMPLIFIER (Fig. 310)

Resistors: R1—1-megohm pot; R2—2,200 ohms; R3—1,000 ohms; R4—500,000 ohms; R5—100,000 ohms; R6, R7—500,000-ohm pots, stacked; R8—1,000 ohms, 1 watt; R9—2,200 ohms, 1 watt; R10—1,000-ohm wire-wound pot

Capacitors: C1, C5, C8—.1-μf 400-volt tubular; C2, C3—25-μf 50-volt electrolytic; C6, C7—.0071-μf 500-volt mica (see text); C4—20-uf 450-volt electrolytic

Transformer: T—2:1 audio interstage
Tube: 12AX7
Socket: 9-pin miniature
Miscellaneous: J1, J2, J3, J4—terminal connectors

Fig. 310. *This amplifier can be tuned to reject any signal from 50 to 10,000 cycles.*

calibration since this potentiometer is adjusted for additional rejection and its settings ordinarily have no effect on the settings of R6-R7.

The rejection afforded by this amplifier is better than 70 db (provided a well-ganged control is used for R6-R7) except at frequencies above 7 kc where stray coupling through the system decreases the attenuation.

An alternative use of this tuned rejection amplifier is as an audio-frequency meter. If potentiometer R6-R7 is calibrated accurately, frequencies may be identified simply by reading the dial of the potentiometer at null.

General-purpose ac-dc audio amplifier

Fig. 311 shows a simple ac-dc audio amplifier which is useful for monitoring purposes, amplification for simple receivers and rf detectors, and for common applications such as phonograph and microphone amplification. Its outstanding features are small size and simplicity.

While this amplifier includes none of the extras such as tone control, negative feedback, etc., it is entirely adequate for signal

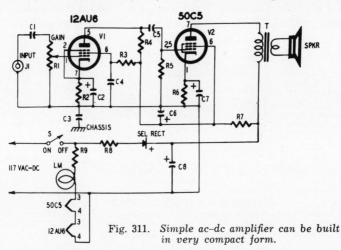

Fig. 311. *Simple ac–dc amplifier can be built in very compact form.*

GENERAL-PURPOSE AC–DC AUDIO AMPLIFIER (Fig. 311)

Resistors: R1—500,000-ohm pot; R2—3,300 ohms; R3—270,000 ohms; R4—220,000 ohms; R5—470,000 ohms; R6—120 ohms, 1 watt; R7—1,000 ohms, 1 watt; R8—470 ohms, 1 watt; R9—300 ohms, 10 watts
Capacitors: C1, C3—.1-μf 600-volt tubular; C2—10-μf 25-volt electrolytic; C4—.05-μf 200-volt tubular; C5—.005-μf 500-volt mica; C6, C8—30-μf 150-volt electrolytic; C7—25-μf 25-volt electrolytic
Transformer: T—output, 2,500 ohms to voice coil (Stancor A-3825 or equivalent)
Tubes: V1—12AU6; V2—50C6; SEL—100-ma selenium rectifier
Sockets: 7-pin miniature (2)
Miscellaneous: S—spst switch; J1—phone jack; LM—No. 40 pilot-lamp assembly; PM speaker

and voice communication purposes and is not unpleasant to the ear. At 155 millivolts rms input (at the maximum-volume setting of gain control R1), power output of the amplifier is close to the 1.9 watts rated for the 50C5 tube.

For safety from electric shock, no direct connection is made to the chassis. The B-minus point of the ac-dc power supply is bypassed to chassis through C3 only. In certain applications, especially instrumentation, in which interaction via the power line is to be avoided, a 1-to-1 isolation transformer may be inserted between the ac outlet and the amplifier power plug.

Experimental magnetic amplifier

Amateur experimentation with magnetic amplifiers usually is thwarted by inability to obtain the special core materials ordinarily required. However, fair magnetic amplifier action can be secured with 60-cycle circuits embodying conventional power transformers. This action is sufficient for numerous interesting and useful control purposes and is more than adequate for educational and demonstration projects.

In Fig. 312, amplifier transformers T1 and T2 are small power transformers of the type designed for radios and amplifiers. Their

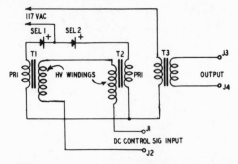

EXPERIMENTAL MAGNETIC AMPLIFIER (Fig. 312)

Transformers: T1, T2—117-volt primary, 250– 800-volt secondary; T3—117 volts, 1:1 ratio

Rectifiers: SEL1, SEL2—500-ma selenium
Miscellaneous: J1, J2, J3, J4—terminal connectors

Fig. 312. *Circuit diagram of magnetic amplifier.*

primary windings are 115 volts and their secondaries from 250 to 800. The entire secondary winding is used, center taps being taped and tucked out of reach. Any filament windings likewise are taped and tucked away.

The two high-voltage secondaries are connected in series-bucking. If the two secondaries were exactly alike, no ac voltage would appear at the dc CONTROL SIGNAL INPUT terminals. But, since in practice they will not be identical, a small voltage will be present at these terminals. The two power-type selenium rectifiers should be matched in characteristics as closely as possible. Transformer T3 couples ac power to the load. Its characteristics will depend largely upon what type of load is employed. Usually a 115-volt isolating transformer with a 1-to-1 turns ratio will suffice.

The two high-voltage windings are connected to the dc control input. With no dc signal input, the cores of T1 and T2 are saturated by the direct current flowing in the primary windings from the rectifiers and the power line. This saturation lowers the primary inductance and therefore the impedance in series with the power line and the primary of T3. A high voltage accordingly is applied to the T3 primary.

When dc control current is applied in the proper polarity, it will buck this saturation and increase the impedance of the primaries of T1 and T2. Since this adds impedance to the path between the power line and the primary of T3, the voltage across the latter now increases. Amplification results from the action of a small amount of dc control power in controlling a large amount of ac power. Power amplifications of 1,000 or more (60 db +) may be obtained with small replacement-type power transformers. Somewhat higher power gains have been reported by some experimenters using photoflash and television power transformers.[3]

In the beginning, the transformers must be poled correctly. To do this:

1. Connect the two primaries in parallel but omit the rectifiers.

2. Connect the two high-voltage secondaries in series, leaving the two open ends.

3. Connect the paralleled primary circuit to a low-voltage ac source (not more than 2 volts, for safety from dangerous electric shock). Do not use the line voltage.

4. Connect a high-impedance ac voltmeter to the two free secondary leads.

5. If the secondaries are properly connected in phase opposition, the only voltage reading obtained will be the small potential due to unbalance between the two secondaries.

6. If, instead, the voltage is appreciable, the secondaries are in series-aiding and their connections must be reversed.

7. Finally, insert the rectifiers. Now a somewhat higher "zero-voltage" reading will appear, due to dissimilarity of the rectifiers.

8. After connection of T3 and the power-line input, the setup is ready for operation.

Remember that magnetic amplifier response is a function of the supply frequency. The higher the desired response, the higher must be the supply frequency. In the simple circuit shown in Fig. 312, it is 60 cycles and a few cycles of this frequency (usually 5) actually are required for the amplifier to respond completely to a suddenly applied control signal.

---

[3] "Magnetic Amplifier Uses Conventional Inductors," by A. I. Bennet, Jr., Electronics; January, 1954; page 181.

Z-axis amplifier for oscilloscope

Many of the older-model service type oscilloscopes have no provision for intensity modulation (Z-axis input) or retrace blanking. Both of these features are very desirable, whether the oscilloscope is used professionally or on an amateur basis.

A single R-C coupled amplifier stage can be added to an existing oscilloscope to provide both retrace blanking and amplified Z-axis input. There is ample room inside any of the older oscilloscopes for addition of such a stage.

Fig. 313 shows the circuit of the Z-axis amplifier employing a 6AU6 miniature pentode. Plate, screen and heater voltages are taken from either the vertical- or horizontal-amplifier circuit.

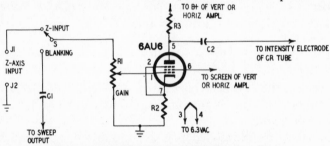

Z-AXIS AMPLIFIER FOR OSCILLOSCOPE (Fig. 313)

Resistors: R1—500,000-ohm pot; R2—820 ohms; R3—100,000 ohms
Capacitors: C1—100-μμf 500-volt mica; C2 —.1-μf 2,000-volt (or more) tubular
Tube: 6AU6
Socket: 7-pin miniature
Miscellaneous: S—spdt switch; J1, J2—terminal connectors

Fig. 313. *Circuit for providing retrace blanking and amplified Z-axis input.*

The dc voltage required for the plate is 250-300, for the screen 100-150. The signal output is coupled from the 6AU6 plate through a 0.1-μf 2,000-volt capacitor (C2) to the intensity electrode of the cathode-ray tube.

The $\frac{1}{2}$-megohm potentiometer (R1) is the Z-axis gain control. Adjustment of this governs the degree of blanking or the amount of intensity modulation. For best response of the single-stage amplifier, cathode resistor R2 is unbypassed.

When the selector switch S is in its upper position, the amplifier input is connected directly to a binding-post terminal on the front panel of the oscilloscope. Any desired signal voltage for intensity modulation of the cathode-ray beam may be applied between this terminal and ground. When switch S is in its lower position, the amplifier input is coupled, through the 100-μμf capacitor, C1, to the output of the oscilloscope sweep oscillator.

In most of the older instruments, this connection will be made to the plate of the 884 sawtooth oscillator tube. With the switch in this position, the sawtooth flyback blanks the trace during the flyback interval.

To minimize hum pickup, all leads in the input portion of the Z-axis amplifier must be kept as short as possible. This may be accomplished easily by mounting the z-axis input binding post, switch S and potentiometer R1 close together on the front panel of the oscilloscope and mounting the 6AU6 socket as close as possible to them. The longest lead in the circuit will be the one running from capacitor C2 to the cathode-ray tube. This lead must be shielded and should be run as far as possible from any ac leads. In some instruments, shielding the 6AU6 tube may be helpful.

Single-stage dc amplifier

Dc amplifiers are notorious for their tendency to drift. In high-gain amplifiers of this type, drift is pronounced and extraordinary measures must be applied to reduce it.

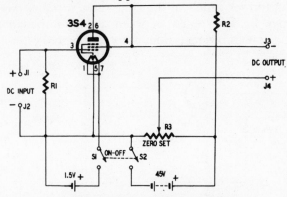

SINGLE-STAGE DC AMPLIFIER (Fig. 314)

Resistors: R1—1 megohm; R2—82,000 ohms; R3—10,000-ohm wirewound pot

Tube: 3S4

Socket: 7-pin miniature

Miscellaneous: S1, S2—dpst switch; J1, J2, J3, J4—terminal connectors; 1½-volt battery; 45-volt battery

Fig. 314. *Single-stage amplifier has voltage gain of 5.*

Drift in a single-stage amplifier is small. However, this type of circuit has insufficient gain for industrial purposes. Experimental applications, on the other hand, often can make profitable use of the lower gain.

Fig. 314 is the circuit of a single-stage dc amplifier that supplies a voltage gain of 5. Operated into a high-resistance load (dc vacuum-tube voltmeter, dc oscilloscope or recorder) the maximum signal which may be applied to the input terminals is 1 volt dc. The corresponding maximum output signal is 5 volts dc.

A triode-connected 3S4 miniature power tube is employed. Batteries are used for maximum stability and independence from the power line. The output circuit contains a four-arm resistance bridge for setting the no-signal output voltage to zero. The four arms of this bridge are R2, the two halves of zero-set potentiometer R3 (one half on each side of the wiper arm) and the internal plate-to-filament resistance (r_p) of the tube. With zero-signal input, R3 is adjusted to balance the bridge for zero output.

This simple amplifier will find application where a dc voltage gain of 5 is useful. For example, it may be operated ahead of a dc vtvm set to the 1½ volt range. The full-scale sensitivity of the meter then will be 0.3 volt, and 4 millivolts will be readable. A potential of 2 mv will be detectable.

General-purpose af cathode follower

The cathode follower is advantageous as a high-to-low impedance transformer which, at the same time, supplies power gain. Thus, it may be interposed between a high-impedance signal source and a low-impedance line, amplifier or circuit to prevent

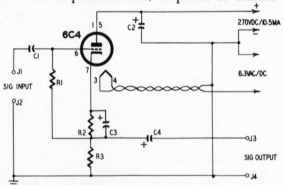

GENERAL-PURPOSE AF CATHODE FOLLOWER (Fig. 315)

Resistors: R1—1 megohm; R2—820 ohms; R3 —1,000 ohms

Capacitors: C1—.1-μf 500-volt mica; C2— 8-μf 450-volt electrolytic; C3—50-μf 25-volt

electrolytic; C4—100-μf 25-volt electrolytic
Tube: 6C4
Socket: 7-pin miniature
Miscellaneous: J1, J2, J3, J4—terminal connectors

Fig. 315. *Cathode follower for use in audio-frequency applications.*

heavy loading of the source. The cathode follower often is built into a probe to be operated ahead of various low-impedance input devices. Because of its high order of degeneration, the cathode follower has excellent frequency response and introduces negligible harmonic distortion. Its output signal is in phase with the input signal.

Fig. 315 shows the circuit of a utility cathode follower with 1-megohm input and 300-ohm output. Using a 6C4 miniature triode, it has a voltage gain of 0.65 and is useful throughout the audio spectrum. The operating voltage requirements are 270 volts dc at 10.5 ma and 6.3 volts ac or dc at 150 ma. These voltages usually can be obtained from the instrument with which the cathode follower is used.

The required dc grid bias of —8.5 volts is developed across the upper section of the cathode resistance network (R2). This section is heavily bypassed by capacitor C3. Resistance section R3 is protected from the short-circuiting effect of conductive paths in external load devices by the 100-μf coupling capacitor C4.

When small over-all size is not a requirement, the cathode follower may be built into a case with a self-contained low-current power supply. This provides complete portability and allows the device to be used in numerous developmental and troubleshooting setups.

Battery-operated cathode follower

Complete isolation from the power line and minimum inter-

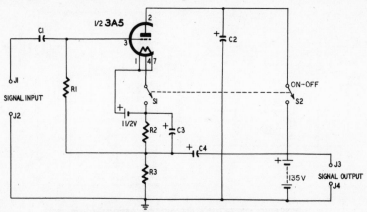

BATTERY-OPERATED AF CATHODE FOLLOWER (Fig. 316)

Resistors: R1—1 megohm; R2—680 ohms, 1 watt; R3—13,000 ohms	**Tube:** 3A5
	Socket: 7-pin miniature
Capacitors: C1—.1-μf 400-volt tubular; C2—8-μf 250-volt electrolytic; C3—50-μf 6-volt electrolytic; C4—100-μf 6-volt electrolytic	**Miscellaneous:** S1, S2—dpst switch; J1, J2, J3, J4—terminal connectors; 1½-volt battery; 135-volt battery (45 volts plus 90 volts)

Fig. 316. *Battery-operated cathode follower is independent of the power line.*

action between an instrument and a test circuit demand battery operation of the instrument.

A battery-operated cathode follower, similar in application to the circuit of Fig. 315, is shown in Fig. 316. This circuit has a 1-megohm input and a 500-ohm output with a voltage gain of 0.90. It is powered by one 1½-volt A-battery cell and one 135-volt B-battery. The A-battery drain is 0.22 ampere and the B-battery drain 3.7 ma. One section of a 3A5 miniature twin triode is used.

The required dc grid bias of —2.5 volts is developed across the upper section of the cathode resistance network (R2). This section is heavily bypassed by capacitor C3. Resistance section R3 is protected from the short-circuiting effect of conductive paths in external load devices by the 100-μf capacitor C4. The dpst ON-OFF switch (S1-S2) interrupts both A and B batteries when thrown to its OFF position.

Because it is battery-operated, this cathode follower may be self-contained with its power supply in a small portable case. This yields a highly flexible accessory for laboratory and shop use.

Loudspeaker-operating transistor amplifier

Fig. 317 shows the circuit of a transistorized audio amplifier which will operate a 4- or 5-inch loudspeaker with good volume. Three transistors are employed: one CK721 as a class-A driver,

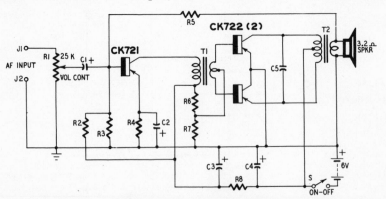

LOUDSPEAKER OPERATING TRANSISTOR AMPLIFIER (Fig. 317)

Resistors: R1—25,000 ohm pot; R2—10,000 ohms; R3—2,200 ohms; R4—820 ohms; R5—20,000 ohms; R6—4,700 ohms; R7—120 ohms; R8—100 ohms, 1 watt

Capacitors: C1, C2, C3, C4—30-μf 6-volt miniature electrolytic; C5—.04-μf tubular

Transformers: T1—transistor class-B driver (Argonne ·AR-109); T2—transistor class-B output (Argonne AR-119)
Sockets: Transistor (3)
Miscellaneous: S—spst switch; 3.2 ohm PM speaker; 6-volt battery; J1, J2—terminal connectors

Fig. 317. *Transistorized audio amplifier will operate loudspeaker.*

and two CK722's in a push-pull class-B output stage. The amplifier delivers approximately 100 mw of audio power and has an overall power gain of 50 db. Total harmonic distortion at full audio output is approximately 5%.

The amplifier is operated from a single 6-volt battery. Because of the low current drain (zero signal, 7.75 ma; maximum signal, 28 ma), four size-D 1.5-volt flashlight cells may be connected in series to form this battery. Base-bias stabilization is provided by voltage-divider networks R2–R3 and R6–R7. The decoupling filter C3–C4–R8 suppresses motorboating.

The input impedance of the amplifier is approximately 1,000 ohms. For higher input impedance, a stepdown transformer may be connected ahead of the AF INPUT terminals. An input signal of only 33 mv rms will drive the loudspeaker to full 100-mw output.

Dry-battery-operated PA amplifier

The amplifier circuit shown in Fig. 318 has been designed for applications where portable dry-battery operation is desired but

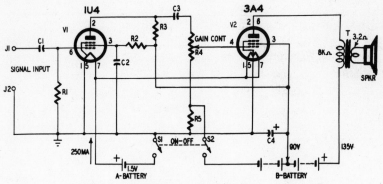

DRY-BATTERY-OPERATED PA AMPLIFIER (Fig. 318)

Resistors: R1—5.1 megohms; R2—1.1 megohms; R3—470,000 ohms; R4—2-megohm pot; R5—470 ohms, 1 watt

Capacitors: C1—.0025-μf 500-volt mica; C2 —.022-μf 200-volt tubular; C3—.002-μf 500-volt mica; C4—12-μf 250-volt electrolytic

Transformer: T—8,000 ohms to voice coil (Merit A-2937 or equivalent)
Tubes: V1—1U4; V2—3A4
Sockets: 7-pin miniature (2)
Miscellaneous: S1, S2—dpst switch; J1, J2—terminal connectors; 1½-volt battery; 45-volt battery; 90-volt battery

Fig. 318. *Amplifier suitable for light-duty PA work.*

higher power output and over-all gain are required than are obtainable with the circuit of Fig. 317.

This amplifier delivers 0.6-watt output for an input signal of 55 millivolts rms. The power output tube is a 3A4 pentode preceded by an R-C-coupled 1U4 voltage-amplifier pentode. Battery requirements are 1-1/2 volts at 250 ma, 90 volts at 10 ma, and 135 volts at 14.9 ma. The 90-volt potential for the screen of the 3A4 and the plate and screen of the 1U4 is obtained from a tap on the 135-volt plate battery. The required fixed dc grid bias of −7½ volts for the 3A4 is developed by plate and screen current flow through the 470-ohm resistor R5.

The only controls are the gain (volume) potentiometer R4 and the dpst ON-OFF switch S1-S2. In its OFF position, the switch interrupts both A- and B-battery circuits.

In the construction of this amplifier, it is advisable to use cushion type tube sockets to minimize microphonics. Filament-type tubes in a high-gain amplifier of this sort give rise to considerable ringing when subjected to vibration. When the sockets are not cushioned, vibrations from a self-contained loudspeaker often will set up a troublesome howl due to acoustic feedback.

This amplifier is suitable for light-duty portable PA and megaphone applications and for use in conjunction with electronic musical instruments.

oscillators

A N oscillator is an electronic type of ac generator. Early experimenters often referred to the oscillator as a generator without moving parts. In modern electronics, oscillators sometimes are called signal generators.

Oscillators are the basis of radio transmitters, high selectivity in receivers, electronic musical instruments, remote control devices, much electromedical equipment and precision measuring devices.

Audio-frequency oscillators generate frequencies up to 20,000 cycles per second, while radio-frequency oscillators take over at 20,000 cycles and generate frequencies up to a point of several thousand-million cycles.

This chapter describes several special-purpose oscillator circuits in both the audio- and radio-frequency categories. These circuits will be useful to the amateur, experimenter and student.

Neon-bulb audio oscillator

When only a tone source is needed and low-distortion output and long-term frequency stability are not requirements, a simple variable-frequency neon-bulb oscillator will be satisfactory. The output waveform is approximately sawtooth in shape.

Fig. 401 shows a neon-bulb oscillator circuit in which potentiometer frequency control is used. The circuit is tunable from 700 to 2,300 cycles. The frequency control, a 0.5-megohm potentiometer, can be provided with a dial indicating the approximate frequency. Signal output voltage into a high-impedance load is approximately 50 volts peak.

Lower frequencies may be obtained by increasing the size of the capacitor, C1. Similarly, higher frequencies result from decreasing this capacitance.

Since only 90 volts dc are required for operation of the circuit, there will be some temptation to use an ac-dc type of power supply. However, this practice is discouraged in this instance unless

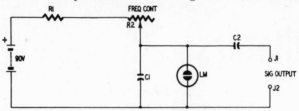

NEON-BULB AUDIO OSCILLATOR (Fig. 401)
Resistors: R1—470,000 ohms, 1 watt; R2— 1-μf 200-volt tubular
500,000-ohm pot   Miscellaneous: LM—NE-48 neon bulb assem-
Capacitors: C1—.001-μf 500-volt mica; C2—   bly; J1, J2—terminal connectors

Fig. 401. *Neon-bulb oscillator supplies sawtooth waveform output.*

an isolating transformer is employed, since the direct connection of the signal output terminal back to the power line creates a serious shock hazard as well as an annoying hum problem. The complication of a transformer-isolated power supply ordinarily will outweigh the simplicity and inexpensiveness of the neon-bulb oscillator.

Code-practice oscillators

Fig. 402 shows several circuits for code-practice oscillators. Each of these has been designed for maximum utility and economy.

Ac-operated type

The circuit shown in Fig. 402-a is powered by an ac-dc type of dc supply using the rectifier section of the 117L7-GT tube. The pentode section is used as the oscillator.

In spite of its ac-dc supply, this oscillator is entirely safe since no part of the key and headphone circuit is connected to the power line. Transformer T provides the isolation.

The operating frequency is governed by capacitor C5 and the inductance of the G-G winding of transformer T. The circuit will oscillate even with no capacitor because of the self-capacitance of the winding. This frequency will be between 400 and

1,000 cycles for most interstage transformers. If it is too high for the reader's satisfaction, it may be reduced by connecting C5 into the circuit.[1] The higher the capacitance of C5, the lower

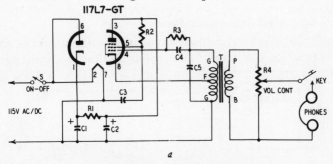

CODE-PRACTICE OSCILLATORS (Fig. 402)

Ac-operated type	(Fig. 402-a)
Resistors: R1—2,000 ohms, 5 watts; R2—110,000 ohms, 1 watt; R3—100,000 ohms, 1 watt; R4—50,000-ohm pot	**Transformer:** T—2:1 audio interstage, single plate-to-push-pull grids
	Tube: 117L7-GT
Capacitors: C1, C2—10-μf 150-volt electrolytic; C3—.1-μf 400-volt tubular; C4—.001-μf 500-volt mica; C5—see text	**Socket:** octal
	Miscellaneous: S—spst toggle switch; high-impedance magnetic phones; telegraph key

Fig. 402-a. *Code-practice oscillator using Hartley circuit.*

will be the frequency. If oscillation is not obtained readily, reverse the outside leads of the center-tapped winding of the transformer.

Battery-operated tube type

Battery operation is preferred for maximum portability and for field use. Fig. 402-b shows a simple transformer-feedback circuit operated from one 1½-volt and one 22½-volt battery. The 1U4 tube is triode-connected by means of the jumper between the plate and screen terminals of its socket.

The operating frequency is governed by capacitor C1 and the inductance of the G-F winding of transformer T. Oscillation will occur at some frequency between 400 and 1,000 cycles even without a capacitor because of the self-capacitance of the transformer winding. If this frequency is too high, it can be reduced by connecting C1 into the circuit. The higher the capacitance of C1, the lower will be the frequency. If oscillation is not readily ob-

---

[1] It is not practical to state a specific value for C5 in Fig. 402-a, C1 in Fig. 402-b or C1 in Fig. 402-c since the values are determined by the inductance of the transformer being used as well as the oscillation frequency desired. This is shown by formula to be: $C = 1/39.5\ f^2L$, where C is in farads, L in henries and f (oscillation frequency) in cps.

tained, the transformer probably is incorrectly connected. The remedy is to reverse the connections of either the primary (P-B) or the secondary (G-F).

Battery-operated transistor type

Low-priced junction transistors are especially attractive for use in code-practice oscillators because of the low dc drain of these

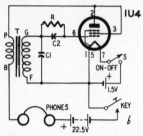 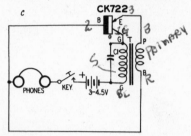

Battery-operated tube type (Fig. 402-b)

Resistor: R—270,000 ohms

Capacitors: C1—see text; C2—300-$\mu\mu$f 500-volt mica

Transformer: T—audio interstage, single plate to single grid

Tube: 1U4

Socket: 7-pin miniature

Miscellaneous: S—spst toggle switch; high-impedance magnetic phones; telegraph key; 22½-volt battery; 1½-volt battery

Battery-operated transistor type (Fig. 402-c)

Capacitor: C—see text

Transformer: T—audio interstage, single plate to single grid

Transistor: CK722

Socket: Transistor

Miscellaneous: magnetic phones, 2,000 ohms or higher; telegraph key; 3–4½-volt battery

Figs. 402-b, -c. *The circuit at the left uses a tube in a regenerative feedback circuit. A transistorized version is shown in the circuit at the right.*

transistors and their ability to operate for long periods from miniature batteries. The small size of the power supply, transistor and associated components makes possible an unusually compact oscillator.

Fig. 402-c shows a transformer-feedback type of code-practice oscillator employing the CK722 transistor. Operating from a single battery, no on-off switch is needed since no current flows until the key is depressed.

As in the previous oscillators, the operating frequency is governed by capacitance C1 and the inductance of the G-G winding of transformer T. Even without C1, the circuit will oscillate at some frequency because of the self-capacitance of winding G-G. This frequency will be lowered by addition of C1. The higher the capacitance of C1, the lower will be the frequency. If oscillation is not obtained readily, reverse either the primary (P-B) or secondary (G-G) connections.

Self-excited 100-kc oscillator

Fig. 403 is the circuit of a simple 100-kc rf oscillator intended primarily as a standard-frequency spot-signal source. It can be set closely to 100 kc by zero-beating against WWV standard-frequency signals by means of the inductance adjustment.

The Colpitts oscillator circuit is employed with a slug-tuned adjustable inductor L. With the capacitances specified for C1 and C2, this coil is set to 3.4 millihenries for 100-kc operation. It may be set to 13.5 millihenries for 50-kc oscillation.

This oscillator is designed to operate into a high-impedance load although it will deliver appreciable signal voltage even when feeding a low impedance, such as a 600-ohm receiver input. In

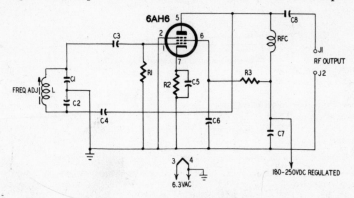

SELF-EXCITED 100-KC RF OSCILLATOR (Fig. 403)

Resistors: R1—1 megohm; R2—470 ohms; R3—62,000 ohms, 1 watt

Capacitors: C1—.003-μf 500-volt mica; C2, C8—.001-μf 500-volt mica; C3, C4—.01-μf 500-volt mica; C5—.005-μf 500-volt mica; C6—.02-μf 400-volt tubular; C7—.05-μf 400-volt tubular

Coils: L—2–18-mh tunable inductor (Miller No. 19-5596 or equivalent); RFC—80-mh rf choke (Meissner No. 19-5596 or equivalent)

Tube: 6AH6

Socket: 7-pin miniature

Miscellaneous: J1, J2—terminal connectors

Fig. 403. *Self-excited oscillator using slug-tuned circuit.*

most applications, such as frequency standardization, no direct connection will be made between the oscillator and the monitoring device.

For maximum stability, a voltage-regulated dc power supply must be used. However, regulation may be obtained through the use of comparatively simple V-R type tubes.

The C1-C2 capacitance combination is high enough to offset the effects of tube and circuit capacitances. Some improvement in stability is obtained by enclosing coil L and capacitors C1 and C2 inside a shield can.

Crystal-type 100-kc oscillator

Maximum stability in 100-kc standard-frequency oscillators is provided by crystal control. Fig. 404 shows the circuit of a completely self-contained crystal-controlled unit.

In this circuit, the small variable capacitor C1 is the frequency trimmer and allows setting the oscillator frequency to zero-beat with WWV broadcasts.

The voltage-doubler type of power supply employs selenium rectifiers. Elimination of the usual rectifier tube reduces heating

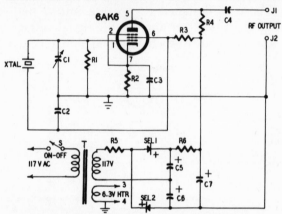

CRYSTAL-TYPE 100-KC OSCILLATOR (Fig. 404)

Resistors: R1—470,000 ohms; R2—3,000 ohms; R3, R4—100,000 ohms; R5—47 ohms, 2 watts; R6—1,000 ohms, 2 watts
Capacitors: C1—50-μμf midget variable; C2—150-μμf 500-volt mica; C3—0.002-μf 500-volt mica; C4—25-μμf 500-volt mica; C5, C6, C7—10-μf 450-volt electrolytic
Transformer: T—1:1 isolation with 6.3-volt

filament winding (Merit P-3045 or equivalent)
Tubes: 6AK6; SEL1, SEL2—75-ma selenium rectifiers
Crystal: 100-kc (Bliley KV3 or equivalent)
Socket: 7-pin miniature
Miscellaneous: S—spst toggle switch; J1, J2 —terminal connectors

Fig. 404. *Crystal-controlled standard-frequency oscillator.*

inside the oscillator and thus improves its stability. Transformer input, through a midget isolating transformer, provides safety and eliminates interaction through the power line. Operating the voltage doubler directly from the power line, without the transformer, is not recommended.

This oscillator has strong signal output, and its 100-kc harmonics are useful as far as 40 mc when a sensitive receiver or monitor is employed.

Transistorized 100-kc crystal oscillator

The low dc drain of the junction transistor, its small size and its ability to operate satisfactorily with a miniature battery suit this transistor to use in a miniature standard-frequency oscillator.

Fig. 405 is the circuit of a 100-kc crystal oscillator using a CK722 transistor. This is a common-base circuit with collector tuning. A variable resistor R2 is provided in the base return

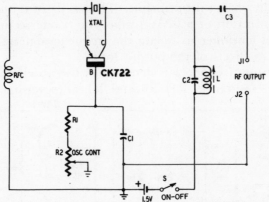

TRANSISTOR-TYPE 100-KC CRYSTAL OSCILLATOR (Fig. 405)

Resistors: R1—2,200 ohms; R2—250,000-ohm pot
Capacitors: C1—.01-μf mica; C2—250-μμf mica; C3—25-μμf mica
Coils: L—4–30-mh tunable inductor (Miller No. 6315 or equivalent); RFC—80-mh rf choke (Meissner No. 19-5596 or equivalent)
Transistor: CK722
Socket: Transistor
Crystal: 100-kc (Bliley KY3 or equivalent)
Miscellaneous: S—spst toggle switch; J1, J2 —terminal connectors; 1½-volt battery

Fig. 405. *Crystal oscillator circuit using a transistor.*

circuit to adjust for strong oscillation with an individual transistor. The output-voltage amplitude and, to a small extent, the frequency will be governed by adjustment of inductor L, the variable member of the L-C2 tuned circuit.

Potentiometer R2 must be adjusted for highest oscillation amplitude, as observed with an oscilloscope or rf vacuum-tube voltmeter connected to the rf output terminals. The setting of R2 also determines the ease and certainty with which the oscillator starts upon closing the switch. After R2 is set correctly, inductor L next is adjusted for zero beat with WWV.

The open-circuit rf output voltage will vary from 0.25 to 0.60 volt rms, depending upon the characteristics of the individual transistor. The dc drain will be less than 25 microamperes for most CK722 transistors.

Single-frequency phase-shift af oscillator

In the phase-shift oscillator, the 180-degree phase reversal required for oscillation is obtained by means of three cascaded R-C legs, each supplying 60 degrees of shift. The oscillator circuit essentially is a class-A amplifier with feedback provided through this phase-rotating network.

Fig. 406 shows a single-frequency, sine-wave oscillator circuit employing the phase-shift principle. The oscillator is built around the pentode section of a 6AW8 tube, the triode section serving as an output amplifier to isolate the frequency-determining R-C network from effects of the output load.

The operating frequency is determined by capacitances C3, C4 and C5 and resistances R5, R6 and R1. Progressing from the

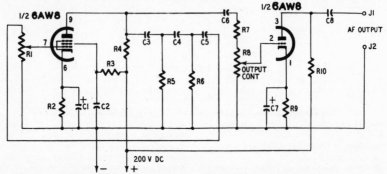

SINGLE-FREQUENCY PHASE-SHIFT AF OSCILLATOR (Fig. 406)

Resistors: R1—50,000-ohm pot; R2—510 ohms; R3, R7—470,000 ohms; R4, R10—100,000 ohms; R5, R6—50,000 ohms, 1 watt 1%; R8—500,000 ohm pot; R9—1,000 ohms

Capacitors: C1, C7—10-μf 25-volt electrolytic;

C2, C8—.1-μf 400-volt tubular; C3, C4, C5—.0018-μf mica (.001-μf and 800-μμf in parallel); C6—.02-μf 400-volt tubular

Tube: 6AW8

Socket: 9-pin miniature

Miscellaneous: J1, J2—terminal connectors

Fig. 406. *Sine-wave oscillator utilizes phase-shift circuitry.*

pentode plate back to its grid, the first 60 degrees of shift are provided by C3-R5, the next by C4-R6 and the last 60 degrees by C5-R1. Since the amplitude of the voltage fed back to the grid will be excessive and therefore will degrade the waveform unless reduced, resistance R1 is made a potentiometer for close adjustment of the grid-signal voltage for best sine-wave output.

The R and C values given for the phase-shift network in Fig. 406 are for 1,000-cycle operation (within 2%). For other frequencies C = 1/10.88fR, R = 1/10.88fC and f = 1/10.88RC. In each case, C is in farads, f in cps and R in ohms.

After R1 is set, it needs no readjustment until tubes are changed or the waveform becomes distorted from some other cause. The output voltage amplitude is controlled by potentiometer R8.

Single-frequency af oscillator with inductive tuning

Fig. 407 shows a simple twin-triode cathode-coupled oscillator circuit employing an adjustable inductor for close adjustment of the single operating frequency.

In this circuit, the frequency is determined by capacitance C3 and inductance L. With the .005-μf value given for C3, the operating frequency is 1,000 cycles when L is adjusted to 5 henries.

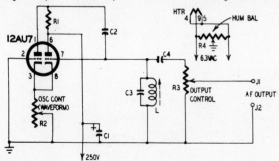

SINGLE-FREQUENCY AF OSCILLATOR USING VARIABLE INDUCTOR (Fig. 407)

Resistors: R1—68,000 ohms, 1 watt; R2—2,000-ohm wirewound pot; R3—100,000-ohm pot; R4—100-ohm wirewound pot

Capacitors: C1—8-μf 450-volt electrolytic; C2, C4—.1-μf 400-volt tubular; C3—.005-μf 500-volt mica

Coil: L—5-h tunable choke (UTC VIC-15 or equivalent)

Tube: 12AU7

Socket: 9-pin miniature

Miscellaneous: J1, J2—terminal connectors

Fig. 407. *Twin-triode cathode-coupled audio-frequency oscillator.*

This adjustment is made with an Allen wrench. With L set to 5 henries, capacitor C3 may be chosen for other frequencies by means of the formula: $C = 1/197.5f^2$ where C is in farads and f in cps. The lowest recommended capacitance is 200 $\mu\mu$f for 5,000 cycles and the highest is 2 μf for 50 cycles.

Potentiometer R2 is set for cleanest output waveform; potentiometer R4 for minimum hum. Output amplitude control R3 is coupled (through C4) across the tuned circuit. For this reason, heavy loads, especially inductive and capacitive, will tend to detune the oscillator.

Grid-dip oscillator

The utility of the grid-dip oscillator is well known. Many variations of this instrument have appeared but all exploit the same principle—the sensitivity of dc grid current in a self-excited oscillator.

Fig. 408 shows the circuit of a grid-dip oscillator utilizing miniature components and employing an electron-eye tube as the indicator. A 6AF4 high-frequency triode is used in the Hartley oscillator circuit. Four plug-in oscillator coils cover the frequency range from 1,200 kc to 135 mc. The dc power supply includes a miniature isolating transformer T, a selenium rectifier and a miniature voltage regulator tube (0B2).

In operation, the shadow of the 6E5 electron-eye tube opens up to indicate resonance or dip. Adjustment of potentiometer

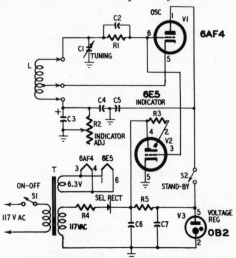

GRID-DIP OSCILLATOR (Fig. 408)

Resistors: R1—50,000 ohms; R2—12,500-ohm wirewound pot; R3—1 megohm; R4—47 ohms, 2 watts; R5—1,500 ohms, 5 watts

Capacitors: C1—140-$\mu\mu$f midget variable; C2—100-$\mu\mu$f 500-volt mica; C3—25-μf 50-volt electrolytic; C4—.1-μf 400-volt tubular; C5—.01-μf 500-volt mica; C6, C7—dual

20-μf 150-volt electrolytics
Coils: See table F on page 77
Transformer: T—isolation (Merit P-3045 or equivalent)
Tubes: V1—6AF4; V2—6E5; V3—0B2; SEL—250-ma selenium rectifier
Sockets: 7-pin miniature (2); 6-contact
Miscellaneous: S1, S2—spst toggle switches

Fig. 408. *Grid-dip oscillator circuit utilizes electron-eye indicator and voltage-regulator tube.*

R2 closes the eye prior to tuning of the oscillator. As the oscillator is tuned through a coil range, there will be some tendency for the eye shadow to overlap, necessitating a backing off of the setting of R2.

When the standby switch S2 is opened, plate voltage is removed from the oscillator but not from the electron-eye tube. Under these circumstances, the grid-dip instrument can be used as an absorption wavemeter with the electron-eye tube as the indicator. High-level rf voltage across the tuned circuit L-C1, now will close the eye shadow to indicate resonance.

Coil-winding data are given in the following table. In general, these coils are not critical. However, some adjustment may be necessary to cover the 35-135-mc range. If the high-frequency coverage is insufficient, spread the turns of this coil apart slightly to reduce its inductance. Some experimentation with the position of the tap also may be necessary with this coil. Extension of the frequency range above 135 mc may be obtained with an additional coil of a single turn and with a tap placed experimentally.

Table F—GRID-DIP OSCILLATOR COILS

1.2–3.6 mc	70 turns No. 32 enameled wire closewound on 1-inch-diameter plug-in form. Tap 24th turn from ground end
3–11 mc	29 turns No. 24 enameled wire on 1-inch-diameter plug-in form spaced to $3/4$ inch. Tap 10th turn from ground end
10–38 mc	$11\frac{1}{2}$ turns No. 22 enameled wire on 1-inch-diameter plug-in form spaced to $1/2$ inch. Tap 4th turn from ground end
35–135 mc	2 turns No. 22 enameled wire on 1-inch-diameter plug-in form spaced to $3/8$ inch. Tap $3/4$ turn from ground end

Electromechanical oscillator

A simple audio oscillator employing the principle of acoustic feedback may be made with a magnetic headphone, carbon microphone button and audio transformer. This arrangement is shown in Fig. 409.

The microphone button is soldered firmly to the diaphragm of the headphone. When the switch is closed, the current pulse produced in the primary of the transformer induces a voltage across the secondary winding, (P-B) and this voltage is applied to the headphone. Actuation of the diaphragm changes the button resistance and causes a further fluctuation in the primary current. This feedback builds up to a state of oscillation (howl). Audio output voltage is taken from the auxiliary secondary winding G-G. The oscillator circuit operates most efficiently into a high value of load inpedance.

The frequency and purity of the audio voltage generated by this type of oscillator depend largely upon the mechanical characterstics of the headphone diaphragm. A frequency of 500 or

600 cycles appears to be common with most 2,000-ohm headphones having metal diaphragms.

The electromechanical oscillator, or hummer, has its chief application in field testing requiring an inexpensive tone source which is small in size, battery-operated and using neither tubes nor transistors.

Unit crystal oscillator

Amateurs and experimenters often find it worth-while to grind their own quartz crystals from fresh blanks or to regrind surplus crystals to new frequencies.

During the grinding process, the crystal must be tested frequently for frequency and activity to determine how the work is

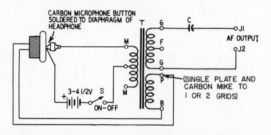

ELECTROMECHANICAL OSCILLATOR-HUMMER (Fig. 409)

Capacitor: C—.1-μf 400-volt tubular
Transformer: T—UTC S7 or equivalent
Miscellaneous: 2,000-ohm magnetic phones;

J1, J2—terminal connectors; 3–4½-volt batteries; S—spst toggle switch; carbon microphone button

Fig. 409. *Simple audio oscillator employs acoustic feedback.*

progressing. For this purpose, a reliable oscillator into which the crystal may be inserted is needed. Fig. 410 is the circuit of such an oscillator. The instrument covers the frequency range from 420 kc to 39 mc with the aid of four plug-in coils. This range includes crystal frequencies extending from the if region to points beyond the 10-meter amateur band.

The oscillator employs a single 6C4 miniature triode and may be operated from any convenient power supply delivering 150 to 250 volts dc at 50 ma and 6.3 volts ac or dc at 0.15 ampere. Several power supplies satisfactory for this purpose are described in Chapter 5.

The plug-in coils are wound on standard four-pin forms. The 420-kc-1.3-mc coil is wound on a 1-1½-inch diameter form (ICA 1108B). All others are wound on 1-inch-diameter forms (Millen 45004). In each instance, L1 is the main coil. Coupling coil L2 consists of two or three turns of the same size wire used for L1 and spaced 1/16 inch from the lower end of L1. Following are the winding instructions for each range covered by L1:

Table G—UNIT CRYSTAL OSCILLATOR COILS

.42–1.3 mc	230 turns of No. 32 enameled wire closewound on 1½-inch-diameter form
1.1–3.8 mc	32 turns of No. 32 enameled wire closewound on 1-inch-diameter form
3.7–12.5 mc	21 turns of No. 22 enameled wire closewound on 1-inch-diameter form
12–39 mc	6 turns of No. 22 enameled wire on 1-inch-diameter form spaced to 3/8 inch

In using the oscillator, the crystal is plugged into the crystal socket. The proper coil to tune to the fundamental frequency of the crystal is inserted into the coil socket. Capacitor C1 then is tuned for resonance. This is indicated either by a dip in the deflection of the milliammeter (M) or by maximum rf voltage at the rf output terminals. Either or both indications may be

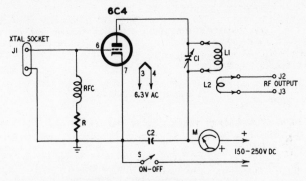

UNIT CRYSTAL OSCILLATOR (Fig. 410)

Resistor: R—56,000 ohms, 1 watt

Capacitors: C1—140-μμf midget variable; C2 —.01-μf 500-volt mica

Coils: L1, L2—plug-in coils, see text; RFC— 2½-mh rf choke

Tube: 6C4

Crystal: see text

Socket: 7-pin miniature; 4-pin for plug-in coils; J1—crystal socket

Miscellaneous: S—spst switch; M—0-50-ma dc meter; J2, J3—terminal connectors

Fig. 410. *Circuit for testing crystals.*

employed. For checking the output (through the output terminals) L2 may be connected to a CW receiver or monitor.

Aside from its use as an aid in crystal grinding, the oscillator is satisfactory as the crystal oscillator stage in transmitters and it may also be used as a single-stage CW transmitter in its own right. In addition it makes a good crystal type test oscillator.

High-frequency transistor rf oscillator

The RCA 2N247 drift transistor will oscillate at frequencies up to 50 mc or better. This makes possible a simple, miniature rf oscillator, the fundamental frequency and harmonics of which may be used in miscellaneous vhf and television testing.

Fig. 411 shows the oscillator circuit. In this arrangement, variable capacitor C4 tunes the oscillator over the frequency range of 28 to 50 mc. Tank coil L1 should be mounted by soldering its ends to lugs fastened to a small polystyrene strip. Coupling coil L2 is mounted $\frac{1}{16}$ inch from the battery end of L1.

The oscillator may be operated at lower radio frequencies by means of higher-inductance plug-in coils. In this way, an rf

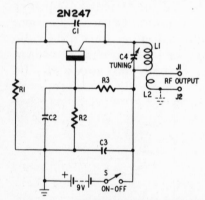

Fig. 411. *Transistor rf oscillator will work at frequencies up to 50 mc or more.*

HIGH-FREQUENCY TRANSISTOR RF OSCILLATOR (Fig. 411)

Resistors: R1—1,000 ohms (see text); R2—3,600 ohms; R3—36,000 ohms

Capacitors: C1—10-$\mu\mu$f mica; C2, C3—.01-μf mica; C4—75-$\mu\mu$f variable

Coils: L1—7 turns No. 20 bare wire airwound ½ inch diameter spaced to ½ inch; L2—2 turns No. 20 bare wire airwound ½ inch diameter spaced thickness of wire. Mount $\frac{1}{16}$ inch from battery end of L1

Transistor: 2N247

Socket: Transistor

Miscellaneous: S—spst switch; 9-volt battery; J1, J2—terminal connectors

test oscillator is obtainable to cover the spectrum from the low if region to 50 mc. However, in wide-range operation of this sort, some adjustment of resistor R1 becomes necessary to insure continuous, strong oscillation throughout the range.

power supplies

MOST electronic equipment contains tubes or transistors. These components require electric power for their operation. In stationary equipment, tube filaments usually are heated by alternating current as a matter of convenience. In both stationary and portable installations, tube plates and screens (and often their control grids as well) are operated with direct current. Transistors are operated entirely with direct current.

The operating requirements of electronic devices extend from potentials of 1 volt or less to several thousand volts and from less than 1 milliampere to several thousand amperes. This energy is obtained from batteries, generators or rectifier devices operated from the commercial power line.

On the following pages are described some practical circuits for power supplies—devices which will furnish the current and voltage required by electronic apparatus. These power supplies may be operated as separate units or they may be built into the equipment which they are to energize.

Variable-voltage bench dc power supply

Dc output voltage from the bench power supply shown in Fig. 501 is continuously variable from 58 to 300 volts. Maximum output current is 150 ma dc at 250 volts, and 100 ma at 300 volts.

Output voltage control is secured through two triode-connected 6L6-G tubes which are connected in parallel to form an electronic variable resistor in series with the dc output. The dc grid bias for these tubes is obtained from potentiometer R. The setting of this potentiometer controls the tube current and thus the dc output voltage.

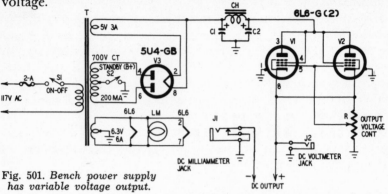

Fig. 501. *Bench power supply has variable voltage output.*

VARIABLE-VOLTAGE BENCH DC POWER SUPPLY (Fig. 501)

Resistor: R—50,000-ohm 4-watt wirewound pot

Capacitors: C1, C2—dual 10-µf 450-volt electrolytic

Transformers: T—350-0-350 volts, 200-ma; 5 volts, 3 amps; 6.3 volts, 6 amps (Thordarson 22R07 or equivalent); CH—6-h 200-ma

filter choke (Thordarson 20C5 or equivalent)

Tubes: V1, V2—6L6-G; V3—5U4-GB

Sockets: octal (3)

Miscellaneous: S1, S2—spst toggle switches; J1—closed-circuit phone jack; J2—open-circuit phone jack; LM—No. 47 pilot-lamp assembly

A closed-circuit jack J1 permits insertion of a dc milliammeter to read output current. An open-circuit jack J2 accommodates a high resistance dc voltmeter for reading output voltage. The standby switch S2 allows the dc output voltage to be switched off without extinguishing the tube filaments.

Germanium type variable dc power supply

Fig. 502 is the circuit of a general-purpose, tubeless, bench-type variable dc power supply. This circuit employs two type 1N158

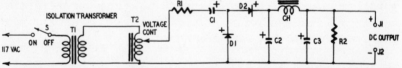

VARIABLE DC POWER SUPPLY USING GERMANIUM POWER RECTIFIERS (Fig. 502)

Resistors: R1—470 ohms, 2 watts; R2—50,000 ohms, 5 watts

Capacitors: C1, C2—100-µf 450-volt electrolytic; C3—10-µf 450-volt electrolytic

Transformers: T1—1:1 100-watt isolation

(Chicago IS-100 or equivalent); T2—Powerstat (Superior 10 or equivalent); CH—8-h 300-ma filter choke (Stancor C2308 or equivalent)

Rectifiers: D1, D2—1N158 germanium power

Miscellaneous: S—spst toggle switch; J1, J2 —terminal connectors

Fig. 502. *Voltage-doubler supply uses isolation transformer.*

germanium power rectifiers in a voltage-doubler circuit. The dc output voltage is continuously variable between zero and 372 volts by means of the Powerstat, T2. At 300 ma dc, the voltage is approximately 270.

For safety and reduction of the effects of interaction, a midget isolating transformer T1 is inserted between the power line and the circuit. The bleeder resistor R2 also is included as a safety measure, serving to discharge the capacitors when the power supply has been operated without a load. For maximum protection and efficiency, do not omit either R2 or T1. Resistor R1 is a peak limiter for protection of the rectifier.

A special advantage of this type of power supply is its instantaneous operation, there being no slow-heating filaments or cathodes in the rectifiers.

Voltage-regulated dc power supply

The stability of some electronic circuits depends to a great extent upon the steadiness of their dc supply voltage. Fig. 503 is

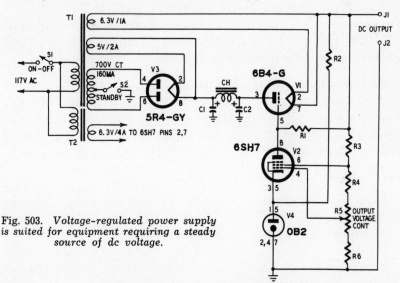

Fig. 503. *Voltage-regulated power supply is suited for equipment requiring a steady source of dc voltage.*

VOLTAGE-REGULATED POWER SUPPLY (Fig. 503)

Resistors: R1—510,000 ohms, 2 watts; R2—75,000 ohms, 2 watts; R3, R6—10,000 ohms, 1 watt; R4—20,000 ohms, 1 watt; R5—15,000-ohm wirewound pot
Capacitors: C1, C2—10-μf 600-volt electrolytic
Transformers: T1—350-0-350 volts, 160 ma; 6.3 volts, 1 amp; 5 volts, 2 amps (Triad R-16-A or equivalent); T2—6.3 volts, 4 amps (Triad F-53X or equivalent); CH—8-h 150-ma filter choke (Thordarson 20C54 or equivalent)
Tubes: V1—6B4-G; V2—6SH7; V3—5R4-GY; V4—0B2
Sockets: octal (3); 7-pin miniature
Miscellaneous: S1, S2—spst toggle switches; J1, J2—terminal connectors

the circuit of an electronically regulated dc power supply suitable for such applications. This supply will maintain output voltage at close values under fluctuating line and load conditions.

The dc output voltage is continuously variable between 180 and 300 volts by means of potentiometer R5. Maximum current drain with good voltage regulation at 300 volts is 50 ma. At 200 volts, 100 ma may be drawn without degrading the regulation.

This circuit is a conventional electronic regulator design. The 6B4-G tube acts as a variable resistor in series with the output. Its resistance depends upon the amount of grid bias it receives, being high for more-negative values and low for less-negative values. The 6SH7 dc amplifier tube determines this bias level and its output, in turn, depends upon its own grid bias received from potentiometer R5. The 0B2 gas tube stabilizes the 6SH7 cathode bias. At any given setting of R5, the 6SH7 grid bias will follow fluctuations in the dc output voltage of the power supply. If this voltage should drop, as might occur with a heavy load, the 6SH7 bias will fall proportionately. This makes the grid voltage of the 6B4-G more positive; it therefore passes more current and the output voltage rises to compensate for the drop that initiated this series of events. The standby switch S2 permits the dc output to be switched off without extinguishing the tube filaments.

Transformerless quadrupler dc power supply

The transformerless circuit in Fig. 504 employs four selenium rectifiers and associated electrolytic capacitors to obtain up to 600 volts dc from the 115-volt ac power line. This circuit will deliver 500 volts at 40 ma and 350 at 100 ma. Operation is instantaneous.

The quadrupling capacitors are C1, C2, C3 and C4. Capacitors C5 and C6 are for filtering only. Resistors R5 and R6 equalize the voltage drop across the capacitors which are series-connected to withstand high dc voltage. Resistors R1, R2, R3 and R4 are peak limiters to protect the rectifiers.

If maximum isolation and shock protection are desired, a 1-to-1 isolating transformer may be inserted between the power line and the input to the circuit.

Rf type high-voltage dc power supply

A radio-frequency type of dc power supply is used for supplying dc voltages up to several thousand volts at low current levels. Its high operating frequency is beyond the range where interference might occur with audio-frequency circuits. This high frequency also permits dc filtering with very small capacitors. Rf type dc power supplies are used in radioactivity instruments, high-voltage breakdown testers, photomultiplier tube circuits and for the biasing of some types of microwave tubes. In this type of power supply, an rf oscillator generates the alternating voltage which is stepped up through a high-turns-ratio transformer and then rectified and filtered.

Fig. 505 shows an rf type dc supply using standard commercial components. The rf oscillator uses a 12AU7 tube with its two

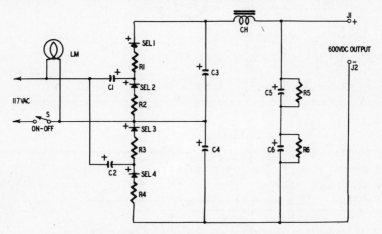

TRANSFORMERLESS QUADRUPLER DC POWER SUPPLY (Fig. 504)

Resistors: R1, R2, R3, R4—10 ohms, 1 watt; R5, R6—470,000 ohms, 1 watt
Capacitors: C1, C2, C3, C4—20-μf 450-volt electrolytic; C5, C6—10-μf 450-volt electrolytic
Choke: CH—10-h 120-ma filter (Stancor

C-325-F or equivalent)
Rectifiers: SEL1, SEL2, SEL3, SEL4—100-ma selenium
Miscellaneous: S—spst toggle switch; LM—117-volt pilot-lamp assembly; J1, J2—terminal connectors

Fig. 504. *Quadrupler supply will furnish an output of 600 volts dc.*

sections in parallel. The rf transformer T1 includes the feedback coils L1 and L2, high-voltage secondary L3 and rectifier filament winding L4. Plate voltage for the 12AU7 is supplied by a voltage tripler composed of selenium rectifiers SEL1, SEL2, and SEL3 and capacitors C3, C4 and C5. Capacitor C6 is for filtering only. Isolation from the power line is provided by the midget transformer T2. If isolation is not desired, this transformer may be omitted and the voltage-tripler circuit operated directly from the line. The 12AU7 filament then must be operated from the 115-volt line through a 683-ohm 25-watt resistor. Connections are made directly to tube terminals 4 and 5.

Neon-oscillator high-voltage dc supply

Fig. 506 is the circuit of a miniature 900-volt dc supply which may be built into small Geiger counters.

The heart of this power supply is the sawtooth oscillator composed of neon bulb LM, resistor R1 and capacitor C2. Sawtooth

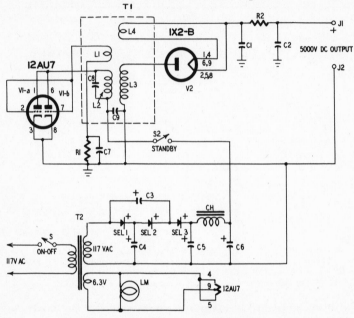

RF TYPE HIGH-VOLTAGE DC POWER SUPPLY (Fig. 505)

Resistors: R1—10 megohms, 1 watt; R2—100,000 ohms, 1 watt
Capacitors: C1, C2—500-μμf 10,000-volt ceramic; C3, C4, C5, C6—80-μf 450-volt electrolytic; C7—.1-μf 600-volt tubular; C8, C9 —contained within T1
Transformers: T1—high-voltage rf (Miller 4525); T2—1:1 isolation (Merit P-3045 or equivalent); CH—16-h 50-ma filter choke (Stancor C1003 or equivalent)
Tubes: V1—12AU7; V2—1X2-B; SEL1, SEL2, SEL3—65-ma selenium rectifiers
Sockets: 9-pin miniature (2)
Miscellaneous: S—spst switch; LM—No. 47 pilot-lamp assembly; J1, J2—terminal connectors

Fig. 505. *High-voltage power supply features an rf oscillator.*

voltage generated by the oscillator is applied to the control grid of the 1U4 tube through capacitor C1. Dc grid bias is adjusted by means of potentiometer R3.

The rapid collapse of the sawtooth voltage generates a high-voltage pulse across the plate choke CH. This pulse is rectified by the high-voltage selenium cartridge SEL and filtered by R4 and C4. The output voltage is controllable over a narrow range by means of potentiometer R3 which, by setting the 1U4 negative grid bias, determines the duration of the pulse across CH.

Transformerless power supplies using semiconductor rectifiers

Weight and space requirements often prohibit the use of power transformers in dc supplies. Tranformerless power supplies are operated directly from the ac power line. When instantaneous operation is desired or heating must be minimized, selenium or

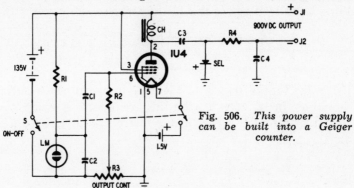

Fig. 506. *This power supply can be built into a Geiger counter.*

NEON-OSCILLATOR HIGH-VOLTAGE DC SUPPLY (Fig. 506)

Resistors: R1—680,000 ohms; R2—470,000 ohms; R3—1,000 ohm wirewound pot; R4—2 megohms, 1 watt
Capacitors: C1—1-µf 200-volt tubular; C2—.01-µf 500-volt mica; C3, C4—.006-µf 1,600-volt tubular
Choke: CH—15-h 20-ma 1,000-ohm midget filter (Triad C-1X or equivalent)

Tube: 1U4
Socket: 7-pin miniature
Rectifier: SEL—high-voltage selenium (Bradley SE-245 or equivalent)
Miscellaneous: S—dpst switch; LM—NE-2 neon lamp assembly; J1, J2—terminal connectors; 67½-volt battery (2); 1½-volt battery

germanium semiconductor power rectifiers are used instead of tubes in these circuits. Germanium rectifiers are preferred for their lower internal voltage drop and better voltage regulation. They also will operate at frequencies up to 50 kc. However, they are somewhat temperature-sensitive. Selenium rectifiers commonly are found in transformerless power supplies in radio, TV and industrial electronic equipment.

In all transformerless dc supply circuits, large capacitors give the best voltage regulation. It is not uncommon, therefore, to find capacitances of several hundred microfarads in each capacitor.

Half-wave rectifier

A typical circuit is shown in Fig. 507. This is the simplest type of transformerless power supply. When followed by a high filter capacitance (8 µf or higher), the no-load dc output voltage of this circuit is approximately 1.41 times the rms ac supply voltage, or 162 volts for a 115-volt line.

The dc ripple corresponds to the power-line frequency and this

87

makes filtering somewhat more difficult than in full-wave rectifier circuits.

Bridge rectifier

Fig. 508 shows a bridge rectifier circuit for single-phase ac input. The advantage of this transformerless circuit over the simple

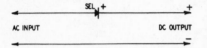

Fig. 507. *Half-wave rectifier using a selenium unit.*

half-wave supply shown in Fig. 507 is its full-wave output. The dc ripple, being at twice the line frequency, is easier to filter.

A disadvantage of the bridge rectifier is its lack of a common

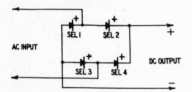

Fig. 508. *Bridge rectifier for single-phase ac input.*

connection between the negative dc output and ac input. In some applications, however, this is of no consequence, or is even an advantage.

Half-wave voltage doubler

Two rectifiers and two capacitors are connected in Fig. 509 to give a dc voltage which under no-load conditions is approximately

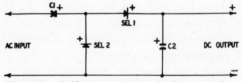

Fig. 509. *Half-wave voltage doubler supplies approximately twice the ac voltage input.*

twice the ac voltage input. Actually somewhat higher dc values are obtained since the capacitors charge to the peak value of the line voltage, less the drop in the rectifiers.

In this circuit, the no-load dc output voltage is approximately 2.82 times the rms input voltage, or 324 volts for a 115-volt line.

Like the simple half-wave rectifier, the half-wave voltage doubler delivers a dc ripple at the line frequency and is harder to filter than is a full-wave circuit.

Full-wave voltage doubler

Fig. 510 shows a doubler circuit which gives performance similar to that of Fig. 509 except that the dc ripple is at twice the ac supply frequency and therefore is easier to filter.

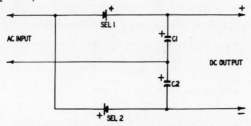

Fig. 510. *Full-wave voltage doubler circuit.*

As in the previous case, the no-load dc output voltage is approximately 2.82 times the rms input voltage, or 324 volts for a 115-volt line.

Half-wave voltage tripler

The circuit in Fig. 511 uses three rectifiers and three capacitors

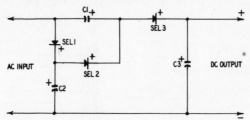

Fig. 511. *Circuit of a half-wave voltage tripler.*

to obtain a no-load dc output voltage equal approximately to 4.23 times the rms input voltage, or approximately 486 volts for a 115-volt line.

Voltage quadrupler

In Fig. 512, four rectifiers and four capacitors are connected to deliver a no-load dc output voltage equal approximately to 5.64 times the rms input voltage, or approximately 649 volts for a 115-volt line. Another practical voltage quadrupler type of power supply was shown previously in Fig. 504.

Explanation of odd step-up values

Some question is apt to arise regarding the odd step-up values listed for the various transformerless supplies: 1.41 for half-wave rectifier, 2.82 for doubler, 4.23 for tripler and 5.64 for the quadrupler. The reason for those high no-load values is that the capacitors charge to a value closely equal to the peak value of the ac input voltage. This is 1.41 times the input voltage for the half-wave rectifier; 2 times 1.41, or 2.82 for the doubler; 3 times 1.41,

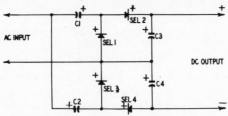

Fig. 512. *Four capacitors and four recti-fiers form this voltage-quadrupler circuit.*

or 4.23 for the tripler, etc. At optimum dc loading, however, the multiplication factor for the doubler is 2, for the tripler 3, etc.

Step-type variable ac voltage supply

In experimental services in which the expense of a Variac is not justified nor its smooth variation of voltage needed, a step-

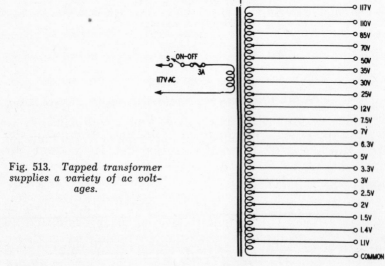

Fig. 513. *Tapped transformer supplies a variety of ac voltages.*

type ac voltage source is adequate. Usually, the voltage steps need not be evenly spaced if a good number of them are available.

A tube-tester type of transformer is convenient as a step-voltage source. This transformer is designed to supply the many different filament voltages in a tube tester. Fig. 513 shows the connections to such a transformer when used as a step-voltage source. The Stancor P-1834-3 unit will supply 20 ac voltages from 1.1 to 117. For convenience in making connections to external devices, pin jacks may be used, as shown in Fig. 513. A twenty-position rotary switch with high current-carrying capacity also might be used to select the voltages.

Filter-tube circuit

The CBS-Hytron type 6216 tube has been designed to replace the bulky 12-henry, 100-ma, 350-ohm, iron-cored choke in a dc power supply filter. This is a miniature tube with 9-pin base.

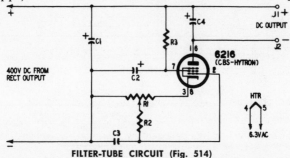

FILTER-TUBE CIRCUIT (Fig. 514)

Resistors: R1—50-ohm wirewound pot; R2—470,000 ohms, 1 watt; R3—62,000 ohms, 1 watt

Capacitors: C1, C2—8-μf 600-volt electro-lytic; C3—.05-μf 400-volt tubular; C4—20-μf 450-volt electrolytic

Tube: 6216

Socket: 9-pin miniature

Miscellaneous: J1, J2—terminal connectors

Fig. 514. *Filter circuit in which a vacuum tube is substituted for a choke.*

Two or more tubes may be connected in parallel to pass more current.

Fig. 514 shows the filter circuit in which the tube replaces the choke. Adjustment of the small potentiometer, R1, controls the amount of ripple in the dc output. With the circuit in operation, this potentiometer is adjusted for the lowest deflection of an oscilloscope or ac vacuum-tube voltmeter connected to the dc output terminals. The adjustment must be made with the power supply delivering maximum dc load current.

Filtering action by the tube depends upon the following factors. The high ac impedance of the tube is in series with the output (load) and limits the ripple current. A portion of the ripple voltage is presented to the control grid through capacitor C3 and is amplified by the tube. This amplified voltage appears across the load in the correct phase to buck the ripple.

At 10 ma dc drain, the dc output voltage is 385 volts. At 100 ma, the voltage drops to 340. The ripple at 100 ma is .03%, in terms of peak ripple voltage vs dc output voltage.

Electronic load resistor

A variable load resistor is necessary when making a volt-ampere test of a power supply. Resistors satisfactory for this purpose are bulky.

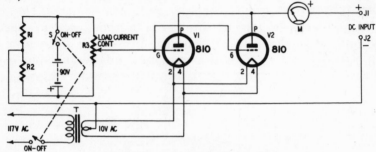

ELECTRONIC LOAD RESISTOR (Fig. 515)

Resistors: R1, R2—4,700 ohms, 2 watts; R3—10,000-ohm wirewound pot, 2 watts

Transformer: T—10-volt 10-amp center-tapped filament (UTC S-62 or equivalent)

Tubes: V1, V2—810

Sockets: 4-pin bayonette

Miscellaneous: S—dpst switch; M—0–500-ma dc meter; J1, J2—terminal connectors; 45-volt battery (2)

Fig. 515. *Two transmitting triode tubes are used as an electronic variable resistor.*

Fig. 515 shows a more compact arrangement in which two parallel-connected type 810 transmitting triode tubes form an electronic variable resistor. In this circuit, the plate-to-filament resistance of the tubes is controlled by varying the grid bias. Load current is indicated by the dc milliammeter.

The grid bias is obtained from a battery through a four-arm bridge circuit composed of resistors R1 and R2 and potentiometer R3. This bridge circuit delivers zero, negative and positive voltages, depending upon the position of the wiper on R3. Increasing positive values lowers the resistance presented to the dc input terminals, while increasing negative values raise this resistance.

Although the bias-voltage source is shown as a battery in Fig. 515, this voltage may be derived also from a well filtered ac-operated power supply.

Compact fixed-bias supply

Fixed dc control-grid bias is required in some tube circuits. It usually is supplied by a battery or an auxiliary ac-operated power supply. Batteries are inconvenient and the power supply is bulky.

The circuit shown in Fig. 516 illustrates a simple method of obtaining fixed bias with five small components that can be fitted easily into existing equipment. The arrangement is a voltage doubler receiving its ac input from the 6.3-volt filament circuit of the device into which the bias unit is built. Two 1N34 germanium diodes are the rectifiers. The storage capacitors are 50-μf, 50-volt electrolytic units. A 1,000-ohm wirewound potentiometer is used to set the dc output voltage to the desired value. This voltage is adjustable from 0 to 13 volts when the ac input is 6.3 volts. The potentiometer shaft can be slotted for screwdriver adjustment since frequent resetting is not necessary.

Since the positive side of the dc output of the bias supply must be grounded in most installations, the ac input cannot also be grounded. Such double grounding would impair the voltage-doubling action of this circuit. This means that any filament-circuit ground connection in the main circuit must be floated.

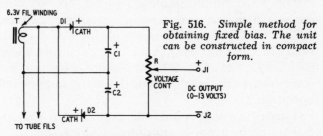

Fig. 516. *Simple method for obtaining fixed bias. The unit can be constructed in compact form.*

FILAMENT-OPERATED BIAS SUPPLY (Fig. 516)

Resistor: R—1,000-ohm wirewound pot	**Transformer:** T—6.3-volt filament winding
	Rectifiers: D1, D2—1N34 germanium diodes
Capacitors: C1, C2—50-μf 50-volt electrolytic	**Miscellaneous:** J1, J2—terminal connectors

In some equipment, this is not permissible because the filament circuit has been grounded to prevent hum. Use of the circuit in Fig. 516, therefore, is limited to apparatus in which the filaments may float ungrounded without trouble.

Miniature power supply for instruments

In low-drain instruments such as simple vacuum-tube voltmeters, preamplifiers, single-frequency oscillators, bridges and parts checkers, the ac-operated power supply often takes up most of the instrument case and accounts for the greater part of the weight.

Since such instruments usually employ only one or two tubes which draw low plate and filament current, the conventional large power transformer, rectifier tube and filter choke are not needed. Fig. 517 shows a miniature line-operated power supply suitable for such installations. Output voltages delivered by this unit are 260 dc at 15 ma, and 6.3 ac at 0.9 ampere. The dimen-

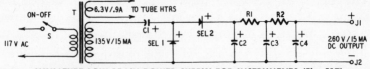

MINIATURE LOW-DRAIN POWER SUPPLY FOR INSTRUMENTS (Fig. 517)

Resistors: R1, R2—3,900 ohms, 2 watts
Capacitors: C1—16-μf 450-volt electrolytic;
C2, C3, C4—triple 16-μf 450-volt electrolytic
Transformer: T—Triad R2C or equivalent

Rectifiers: SEL1, SEL2—20-ma selenium

Miscellaneous: S—spst switch; J1, J2—terminal connectors

Fig. 517. *Small-size line-operated power supply for test instruments.*

sions of the power transformer (Triad R2C) are only 1-3/8 inches high, 1-7/8 inches wide and 1-9/16 inches deep. This unit delivers both 6.3 and 135 volts.

The power supply employs a voltage-doubler circuit embracing the two 20-milliampere selenium rectifiers and storage capacitors C1 and C2. While the dc ripple in this type of circuit is low, additional filtering has been provided by resistors R1 and R2 and capacitors C3 and C4. The miniature selenium rectifiers further contribute to the small size of the power supply and provide cool operation.

This entire supply may be mounted in the space ordinarily demanded by a power transformer alone.

Simple constant-current supplies

The testing and experimental operation of some modern electronic components such as crystal diodes, semiconductor rectifiers, varistors, thermistors, and transistors often require a source of constant direct current. How to obtain such dc is apt to be puzzling to the technician who is in the habit of working with constant-voltage supplies.

Fig. 518 shows three simple methods of obtaining constant direct current. In each case, the scheme is to connect a high resistance in series with a voltage source and the ouput terminals. If this series resistance is many times higher than the resistance of the device under test connected to the output terminals, variations in the resistance of the device will have only negligible effect on the current flow. The output current thus is determined almost solely by the high series resistance R1 and is reasonably constant.

For illustration, consider the resistance Rx of the device under test to be 10 ohms and R1 to be 1,000 ohms. If Rx doubles to 20 ohms (a severe variation), the current in the circuit would decrease by only 1.1%. Without R1 in the circuit, the current would fall to one-half of its initial value, a 50% reduction.

The higher the resistance of R1 with respect to Rx, the more constant will be the output current. However, one can see from a simple application of Ohm's law that the higher the resistance of R1, the higher must be the applied voltage for a given current.

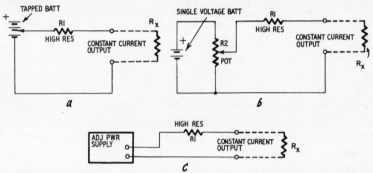

Figs. 518-a, -b, -c. *Three simple methods of obtaining constant direct current.*

A practical procedure for setting up a constant current supply is: (1) Choose R1 to be 100 times the maximum value that Rx is expected to have. (2) Connect R1, Rx and a suitable dc milliammeter in series with a variable-voltage dc source. (3) Vary the voltage until the desired value of current flows in the circuit. (4) Temporarily short-circuit Rx. The current change should not exceed approximately 1% of the initial current value. If it does, R1 must be increased.

In lieu of the practical approach, the system may be designed beforehand in the following manner:

1. Express the desired constant current I in amperes.

2. Express in ohms the maximum expected resistance Rx of the test device.

3. Select R1 to equal 100Rx.

4. Determine the required voltage E from the formula $E = I(R1 + Rx)$ volts. Much closer current regulation is obtained when $R1 = 1,000Rx$ or even $10,000Rx$. However, the voltage may be impractically high in such cases.

Now let us consider a typical problem. A constant current of 10 ma is required in a device whose internal resistance will not exceed 5 ohms. Here, $I = .01$ amp, $Rx = 5$ and $R1 = 500$. Sub-

stituting these values in the formula, we find that $E = .01(500 +$
$5) = .01(505) = 5.05$ volts.

If more constant current is desired, R1 can be chosen equal
to 1,000Rx, whereupon $E = .01(5,000 + 5) = 50.05$ volts (50 volts
in practice).

The output of a constant-current supply may be adjusted to
various desired current levels by adjusting the voltage. The current, then, will hold constant at any of these pre-set values. This
is done in Fig. 518-a by means of a tapped battery, in Fig. 518-b
with a potentiometer across the battery and in Fig 518-c by an
adjustable-output line-operated power supply.

When the external load Rx is disconnected from the simple
constant-current supply, the full dc voltage appears at the output
terminals. This demands caution to prevent electric shock when
the applied voltage is high and the resistance of R1 insufficient
to limit current to a safe value. A prudent rule is to switch off
the supply before making any connections or disconnections to
the output terminals.

Low-drain ac voltage regulator

The inexpensive gaseous-tube circuit shown in Fig. 519 will
deliver a constant output of 75 volts ac to loads not exceeding

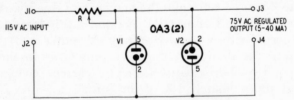

SIMPLE LOW-CURRENT AC VOLTAGE REGULATOR (Fig. 519)

Resistor: R—2,500 ohms, 10 watts, with   Sockets: octal (2)
slider   Miscellaneous: J1, J2, J3, J4—terminal con-
Tubes: V1, V2—0A3   nectors

Fig. 519. *Gas–tube ac voltage regulator circuit.*

3 watts. Ac voltage regulation is desirable for the stable operation of instruments and other critical electronic circuits.

Constant output voltage is provided by the two 0A3 tubes.
These tubes are connected back to back so that one regulates the
positive half-cycle of the ac line voltage and the other the negative
half-cycle.

The 2,500-ohm current-limiting resistor R is set initially in the
following manner.

1. Connect an ac vacuum-tube voltmeter (set to its 100-volt
range) to the output terminals of the regulator circuit.

2. Set the slider on the current-limiting resistor so that this resistor has about three-fourths of its full resistance.

3. Switch on the ac line voltage.

4. Observe the voltmeter reading.

5. Connect a 2,000-ohm 10-watt resistor momentarily to the output terminals.

6. If the meter deflection drops, switch off the power and adjust the slider to decrease the resistance of the current-limiting resistor.

7. Again switch on the power and momentarily connect the 2,000-ohm resistor to the output terminals.

8. Continue these steps until the meter deflection remains substantially at 75 volts as the 2,000-ohm resistor is connected and disconnected at the output terminals.

9. Finally, tighten the slider on the current-limiting resistor.

Pushbutton type high-voltage supply

Each time the pushbutton switch in Fig. 520 is depressed and released, the low-turns winding of the transformer is connected and disconnected from the 1½ volt cell. The resulting current surge through this winding induces a high voltage across the high-turns winding of the transformer.

This action may be utilized to obtain the high voltage required for polarizing a Geiger tube, if the high-voltage pulse is used to

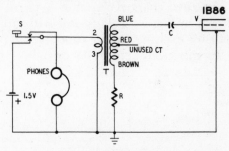

Fig. 520. *High-voltage supply for Geiger counter features pushbutton operation.*

PUSHBUTTON-TYPE HIGH-VOLTAGE SUPPLY IN SIMPLE GEIGER COUNTER (Fig. 520)
Resistor: R—56,000 ohms, 1 watt
Capacitor: C—.1-μf 600-volt tubular
Transformer: T—Stancor A-3856 or equivalent
Tube: V—1B86
Miscellaneous: S—spdt normally closed pushbutton switch; high-impedance magnetic phones; 1½-volt battery

charge a capacitor. An inexpensive speaker output transformer can be used. Fig. 520 shows how the arrangement is employed to supply 300 volts to a 1B86 tube in a simple Geiger counter circuit.

When the pushbutton is depressed momentarily, the high-voltage pulse from the transformer fires the 1B86 tube and charges the 0.1-μf capacitor. The capacitor then remains charged because the Geiger tube now acts as an insulator and breaks the circuit through which the capacitor might discharge. The length of time the capacitor will hold its charge depends upon the insulation of this component and how well the circuit is sealed against moisture in the surrounding air.

When the 1B86 tube is exposed to a radioactive sample, each active particle from the material will fire the gas in the tube causing it to conduct current from the charged capacitor, through the high-turns winding of the transformer and the 56,000-ohm resistor. This, in turn, induces a voltage across the low-turns winding and current flows through the headphones, producing a click. As the sensitivity of the counter dies down, because of depletion of the charge in the capacitor, the pushbutton may be tapped again quickly, one or more times, to restore the capacitor to full voltage. In the normal resting position of the pushbutton, the headphones are connected to the transformer and the instrument is in the listening condition.

The entire plate winding of the small output transformer is used, the center-tap lead being rolled up and tucked out of reach. Input connections are made to transformer lugs 2 and 3.

Battery-capacitor type high-voltage supply

Another charged-capacitor type of high-voltage dc supply is shown in Fig. 521. This unit will supply 900 volts dc at low current for exciting Geiger tubes of the type 1B85.

In this circuit, two 1-μf capacitors first are charged separately

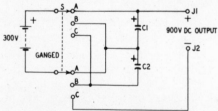

Fig. 521. *Switch-operated high-voltage supply. Capacitors C1 and C2 are charged in series.*

BATTERY–CAPACITOR HIGH-VOLTAGE SUPPLY FOR GEIGER TUBE (Fig. 521)
Capacitors: C1, C2—1-μf 400-volt tubular   J1, J2—terminal connectors; 300-volt minia-
Miscellaneous: S—2-pole 3-position switch;   ture battery

by momentary connection to a miniature 300-volt battery. Each of these capacitors while charged thus becomes a 300-volt source with the polarity shown in Fig. 521. Then, the capacitors are connected in series with each other and the battery to give a total of 900 volts. The length of time each of the capacitors will remain charged to a potential near 300 volts depends upon their insulation and how well the circuit is sealed against moisture.

The charge-and-discharge operation is accomplished by means of a two-pole, three-position switch S. When this switch is in position A, capacitor C1 is connected to the battery and is charged. When the switch is transferred to position B, capacitor C2 is connected to the battery and charged. The lower terminal of C1 is wired to the upper terminal of C2, as shown. When the switch is in position C, the battery is connected in series with the two series-connected capacitors and the output terminals. The polarities then are correct for adding the capacitor and battery voltages.

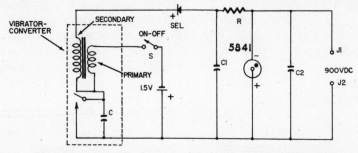

VIBRATOR TYPE HIGH-VOLTAGE SUPPLY FOR GEIGER TUBE (Fig. 522)

Resistor: R—5.1 megohms, 1 watt

Capacitors: C, C1, C2—.1-μf 1,000-volt tubular

Vibrator convertor: Precise Measurements 10MVT

Tube: 5841 Victoreen; SEL—high-voltage selenium rectifier (Bradley SE245 or equivalent)

Miscellaneous: S—spst switch; J1, J2—terminal connectors; 1½-volt battery

Fig. 522. *Vibrator unit forms the basis for a high-voltage supply.*

As the output voltage falls, due to capacitor discharge and evidenced by a decrease in intensity of the Geiger counter, switch S may be flipped back through its ABC sequence to recharge the capacitors. A good practical scheme is to employ a lever type switch (such as Centralab type 1455) with a spring return to keep it normally in position C. A momentary push of this switch will move it automatically from A to B to C. Several quick rockings of the switch usually are necessary to charge the capacitors fully.

Vibrator type high-voltage supply

Fig. 522 is the circuit of a compact, small-sized unit which will supply 900 volts of regulated dc to a type 1B85 Geiger tube.

The basis of this unit is the model 10MVT vibrator-transformer type of converter. This converter is like a miniature spark coil.

Operated from a single 1-½-volt size-D flashlight cell, it delivers more than 1,000 volts of ac. This is then converted to dc by the small, cartridge type high-voltage selenium rectifier and is held closely to 900 volts by the 5841 regulator tube. This tube has no filament. Filtering action is provided by the 5.1-megohm resistor R and capacitors C1 and C2. Capacitor C eliminates electrical noise (hash) due to sparking of the vibrator contacts, which would interfere with the Geiger amplifiers.

The filaments of the tubes in the Geiger counter circuit may be operated from the same 1-½-volt cell that powers the converter.

Combination bleeder and voltmeter

The requirements for both a safety bleeder and dc voltmeter in a high-voltage power supply can be satisfied by a 0-1 dc milliammeter and a suitable multiplier resistor connected to the dc output terminals.

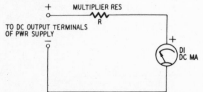

Fig. 523. *Circuit performs dual functions of bleeder and dc voltmeter.*

Fig. 523 shows the circuit of this accessory which can be built into the power supply unit. The multiplier resistor R should have a 2-watt rating. The value of this resistance R will be equal to 1,000 E, where E is the desired full-scale voltage deflection. Thus, for the 1-ma meter to read 0-100 volts, R must be 100,000 ohms. For 1,000 volts, R = 1 megohm; for 5,000 volts, R = 5 megohms; etc. On ranges such as 100, 1,000 and 10,000, voltages may be read directly from the 1-ma scale by mentally adding the correct number of zeros. A special scale may be drawn and installed in the meter, if desired.

This simple device serves efficiently the dual functions of bleeding off dangerous charges from the filter capacitors when the power supply is switched off and in showing the actual dc voltage when the supply is in operation.

Low-cost high-voltage supply for oscilloscopes

Fig. 524 is the circuit of an inexpensive high-voltage dc power supply suitable for 5-inch oscilloscope tubes. This unit will deliver close to 2,000 volts from a small, low-cost, receiver-replacement type power transformer.

A voltage-doubler circuit is employed with the full secondary high-voltage winding of the transformer. The doubler comprises the two 6X4 rectifier tubes, with their plates paralleled, and the two 0.1-μf, 1,000-volt capacitors. Although the capacitances are

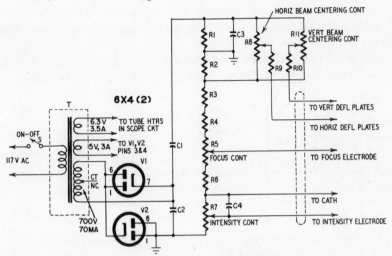

LOW-COST HIGH-VOLTAGE SUPPLY FOR OSCILLOSCOPES (Fig. 524)

Resistors: R1, R2, R5, R9, R10—2 megohms, 1 watt; R3—5.1 megohms, 1 watt; R4, R6—1 megohm, 1 watt; R5, R8, R11—2-megohm pot; R7—1-megohm pot

Capacitors: C1, C2—.1-μf 1,000-volt oil-filled; C3, C4—.25-μf 200-volt tubular
Transformer: T—Thordarson 24R02
Tubes: V1, V2—6X4
Sockets: 7-pin miniature (2)
Miscellaneous: S—spst switch

Fig. 524. *Power supply for use in a cathode-ray oscilloscope.*

low, doubling action is good at the low current drain of a cathode-ray tube and its resistance network. Also, the inherent ripple is low enough to permit hum-free operation without additional filtering.

Replacement transformers rarely have two 6.3-volt filament windings. For that reason, the 6X4 tube heaters are operated from the 5-volt winding, leaving the 6.3-volt winding free for operating the cathode-ray tube. In extensive tests of this power supply, no difficulty has been experienced from operating the 6X4 tubes at this reduced heater voltage.

This power supply is useful also for operating photomultiplier tubes, insulation testing, voltmeter calibration and similar purposes requiring 2,000 volts dc at low current. In such applications, resistors R1 to R10 and the two 0.25-μf capacitors C3 and C4 would be omitted.

Vibrator type power supply

The combination power supply shown in Fig. 525 delivers 300 volts dc at 75 ma. It may be operated, as a vibrator type portable unit, from a 6-volt battery or, as a conventional stationary installation, from the 117-volt ac line. It also supplies a filament voltage of 6 volts dc on battery operation or 6.3 volts ac on power-line operation.

The power transformer has separate primary windings for a 6-volt vibrator and 115 volts ac. Separate on-off switches accordingly

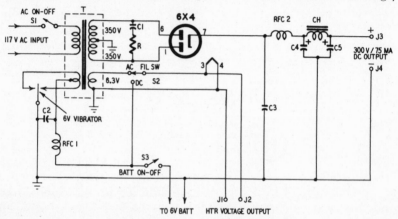

VIBRATOR TYPE POWER SUPPLY (Fig. 525)

Resistor: R—5,600 ohms, 1 watt

Capacitors: C1—.01-μf 1,600-volt vibrator buffer; C2—.5-μf 200-volt tubular; C3—.01-μf 600-volt tubular; C4, C5—dual 10-μf 450-volt electrolytic

Chokes: RFC1—4 μh (Miller 5221 or equivalent); RFC2—2.5 mh (Miller 5222 or equivalent); CH—10-h 175-ma 90-ohm filter (UTC

S-29 or equivalent)

Transformer: T—vibrator power (Stancor P-6166 or equivalent)

Vibrator: 6 volts (Mallory 298 or equivalent)

Tube: 6X4

Socket: 7-pin miniature

Miscellaneous: S1, S3—spst switches; S2—spdt; J1, J2, J3, J4—terminal connectors; 6-volt battery

Fig. 525. *Unusual power supply arrangement permits operation from 6-volt dc source or the ac power line.*

are provided: S1 for power-line operation and S3 for battery operation. A filament-voltage switch S2 is also employed. During power-line operation, it is thrown to its ac position, connecting the tube and terminals to the 6.3-volt winding of the transformer.

The make-and-break action of the vibrator is capable of generating considerable hash interference in sensitive radio and electronic circuits when a supply of this type is battery-operated. This is caused by sparking of the vibrator contacts. To minimize this disturbance, radio-frequency choke RFC1 and capacitor C2 are connected to the vibrator. Also, the buffer capacitor-resistor network C1-R is connected across the high-voltage secondary of the transformer, and a second radio-frequency choke RFC2 and capacitor C3 are inserted in the dc output circuit.

Low-cost isolating transformer

Personal safety and equipment protection often demand the insertion of a 1-to-1 ratio isolating transformer between the power line and equipment.

In some installations, standard isolating transformers, when available, are too large for easy accommodation. In temporary experimental setups, the transformer cost often is unreasonable.

Fig. 526 shows how two filament transformers may be connected back to back to provide the 1-to-1 turns ratio and complete isolation. These transformers are relatively inexpensive and some-

Fig. 526. *Two filament transformers connected back to back can be used as an isolation transformer.*

times are found in shop junkboxes. The two filament windings are connected together. The power line is connected through a spst on-off switch to the high-voltage winding of one transformer and line-level voltage is taken from the high-voltage winding of the other transformer. While 6.3-volt transformers are indicated in Fig. 526, other types can be used as long as the filament voltages are identical in both units.

The two transformers may be mounted side by side in a small box with the switch and an outlet socket to give a compact, inexpensive isolating-transformer setup.

Battery power for electronic equipment

Batteries are employed as the power supply in many types of electronic equipment. They are used also in stationary equipment, especially some test instruments, when operation from the power line would introduce hum or give rise to interaction. Batteries supply smooth direct current which requires no filtering. This greatly reduces the complexity, and sometimes the size, of the power supply.

Because batteries must be replaced periodically and since B-batteries are relatively high-priced, the cost of battery operation has been estimated at 10 dollars per kilowatt hour. In tube-type equipment, the cost of battery operation sometimes is prohibitive and prevents its use altogether. Whenever batteries are used with tubes, switch-off the apparatus when it is not actually in use, to prolong battery life. Although the cost per kilowatt hour remains the same, the battery operation of transistorized equipment is feasible for two reasons: The initial cost of the low-voltage batteries used in transistor circuits (often 1½-volt flashlight cells) is very low and the batteries give long life because of the low current drain of transistors.

Batteries are employed in electronic equipment both directly and indirectly. In the direct application, A-batteries heat the filaments of tubes and B-batteries supply the higher-voltage plate and screen potentials. Except in experimental applications involving short operating periods, the use of banks of series-connected batteries for very high voltages is not economical from either a standpoint of initial cost or replacement. Thus, it is not practical to use batteries directly for the high voltage and high current demanded by transmitter plates and screens. In the indirect application, a low-voltage battery drives a dynamotor or vibrator transformer to supply ac or dc high voltage. (Examples are the automobile radio and mobile transmitter power supplies.) Here, sizable current is drawn from the battery.

Both dry batteries and storage batteries are employed in electronics. The storage battery has the obvious advantage that it is not discarded when discharged. Dry batteries are convenient but short-lived except in transistorized equipment. Conventional storage batteries can supply rather large currents but are heavy, bulky, and often messy. Large banks of small-sized storage batteries series-connected for high voltage seldom are used today.

A battery is the simplest kind of power supply. But it is not one that can be installed and forgotten. Batteries require attention. Dry batteries should be replaced when their full-load voltage has dropped below about 60% of initial voltage—in some applications even sooner. Some dry batteries ooze electrolyte when they have reached exhaustion and must be removed from the equipment immediately before the liquid damages components and wiring.

Use a high-resistance dc voltmeter to test dry batteries. Check under full-load conditions. Storage batteries must be kept full-charged and their outsides clean and dry. Electronic equipment should be protected from gassing by these batteries. The liquid level in the storage cell must be maintained by adding distilled water as required. Use a hydrometer, never a voltmeter, to determine the state of charge of a storage battery.

chapter

6

communications equipment
and accessories

THE first job of electronics was wireless communication, and radio still is an important phase of electronic activity. Many thousands of commercial and amateur radio stations are in daily operation throughout the world. Communications, entertainment, public safety, military operations and national defense all utilize the air waves. Television is a direct outgrowth of the radio industry.

In this chapter, radio communication circuits and accessories of special interest to hams and listeners will be found. We have not delved into a detailed treatment of transmitter and receiver construction since this material is readily available in several amateur handbooks.

Novice CW transmitter

Fig. 601 shows the circuit of a crystal-type, single-tube CW transmitter with self-contained power supply. This is a compact arrangement suitable for use by the novice.

In the 40- and 80-meter bands, the power output will be between 15 and 20 watts. With a good antenna, long-distance code contacts are possible when interference from higher-powered stations is not severe.

Frequencies in the 80-meter band permitted for novice use range from 3700 to 3750 kc and in the 40-meter band from 7175 to 7200 kc. One or more crystals should be obtained on frequencies in these ranges.

Manufactured plug-in coils (L1 and L2) are employed. This keeps construction labor to a minimum. Shunt feed (through blocking capacitor C4) keeps dc off the coils and tuning capacitor C5. This is a safety measure.

The transmitter is tuned-up first without the antenna in the following manner: Insert the crystal and coil for the chosen band, then close switch S. After a 2- to 3-minute warmup period, depress the key; the milliammeter should read approximately 75 ma.

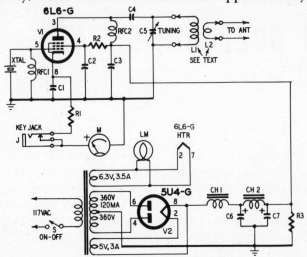

NOVICE CW TRANSMITTER (Fig. 601)

Resistors: R1—220 ohms, 2 watt wirewound; R2—15,000 ohms, 2 watts; R3—60,000 ohms, 10 watts

Capacitors: C1, C2, C3—.01-μf 500-volt mica; C4—150-μμf 500-volt mica; C5—75-μμf variable, .026 inch spacing (National ST-75 or equivalent); C6, C7—dual 15-μf 475-volt electrolytics (Mallory FP258 or equivalent)

Coils: L1, L2—plug-in end-link set—80 meters, Barker & Williamson 80JEL; 40 meters, 40JEL

Chokes: CH1—10½ h, 110 ma (Stancor C1001 or equivalent); CH2—5 h, 100 ma (Stancor C2305 or equivalent); RFC1, RFC2—2½-mh rf

Transformer: T—360-0-360 volts, 120 ma; 5 volts, 3 amps; 6.3 volts, 3.5 amps (Stancor PM-8410 or equivalent)

Tubes: V1—6L6-G; V2—5U4-G

Sockets: octal (2)

Crystal: 3700–3750-kc 80-meter band; 7175–7200-kc 40-meter band

Miscellaneous: S—spst toggle switch; M—0–100-ma dc meter; J—midget closed-circuit phone jack; LM—No. 47 pilot-lamp assembly

Fig. 601. *Crystal type single-tube CW transmitter.*

Now tune capacitor C5 slowly through its range. As the tuning progresses, the meter deflection will dip sharply to 50 ma or less. As C5 is tuned still farther, the reading will rise slowly again to a value near the original 75 ma. The transmitter is considered tuned correctly at the point where the current has just begun to climb out of the low dip. This is the most stable point of oscillation. Now with the antenna connected, retune C5. Note that the dip now is broader than before, due to the loading effect of the antenna. However, the correct operating point still is along the "climb-out" region of the current, as read on the milliammeter scale.

To avoid rf burns, the transmitter should always be switched off before changing coils.

Ham-band regenerative receiver

The regenerative receiver is an excellent unit for the thrifty newcomer to tackle for experience in building communications

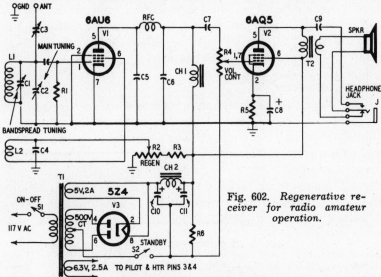

Fig. 602. *Regenerative receiver for radio amateur operation.*

REGENERATIVE RECEIVER (Fig. 602)

Resistors: R1—220,000 ohms; R2—25,000-ohm wirewound pot; R3—18,000 ohms, 2 watts; R4—500,000-ohm pot; R5—330 ohms, 2 watts; R6—50,000 ohms, 5 watt wirewound

Capacitors: C1—50-μμf variable; C2—150-μμf variable; C3—3–30-μμf trimmer; C4—.001-μf 500-volt mica; C5, C6—100-μμf 500-volt mica; C7, C9—.1-μf 400-volt tubular; C8—25-μf 50-volt electrolytic; C10, C11—10-μf 450-volt electrolytic

Coils: L1, L2—plug-in set (I.C.A. No. 1471) (see text)

Chokes: CH1—350-h af-coupling (Thordarson 20C50); CH2—12-h 80-ma filter (Thordarson 20C53); RFC—2.5 mh (National R-100 or equivalent)

Transformers: T1—250-0-250 volts, 75 ma; 5 volts, 2 amps; 6.3 volts, 2.5 amps (Triad R-8A or equivalent); T2—8,500-to-3.2-ohm voice coil (Stancor A-3823 or equivalent)

Tubes: 6AU6; 6AQ5; 5Z4

Sockets: octal; 7-pin miniature (2)

Miscellaneous: S1, S2—spst toggle switches; J—break—make midget phone jack; 3.2-ohm PM speaker; No. 47 pilot-lamp assembly

equipment. While simple, this type of receiver is sensitive. It does not possess the selectivity of the superheterodyne but it is capable of good performance when handled properly.

The circuit in Fig. 602 is completely self-contained for either loudspeaker or headphone operation. The tuning range of this set is 1725 kc to 31.6 mc. Four manufactured plug-in coils (I.C.A.

No. 1471) are used. Each coil provides the windings L1 and L2. General coverage is afforded by the variable capacitor C2; amateur bandspread tuning by the smaller variable trimmer capacitor C1. The antenna trimmer C3 is adjusted for the individual antenna. When this trimmer is set properly, the antenna will exhibit a minimum detuning effect upon the receiver.

This receiver has good sensitivity and volume. Potentiometer R4 adjusts the volume of both headphones and loudspeaker signals. When headphones are plugged in, jack J automatically disconnects the loudspeaker. The regeneration control R2 should be adjusted for maximum sensitivity without oscillation. The standby switch S2 allows the set to be muted during transmissions without extinguishing the tube heaters.

Superhet converter

The construction of a complete superheterodyne amateur receiver seldom is economical. However, many of the advantages of the superhet may be obtained with a converter operated ahead of a broadcast receiver when neither a manufactured nor kit-type set can be afforded.

Fig. 603 is the circuit of a simple one-tube converter. This unit derives its operating voltages from the set to which it is connected and is designed around the 6BE6 pentagrid converter tube. The

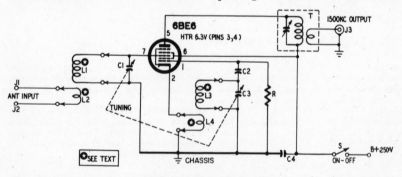

SUPERHET CONVERTER (Fig. 603)

Resistor: R—22,000 ohms

Capacitors: C1, C3—dual 140-μμf 500-volt midget variable (Hammarlund MCD-140-M); C2, C4—50-μμf 500-volt mica

Coils: L1, L2, L3, L4—plug-in type (see table and text)

Transformer: T—1,500-kc converter (Miller 512-W1)
Tube: 6BE6
Socket: 7-pin miniature
Miscellaneous: S—spst toggle switch; J1, J2—terminal connectors; J3—concentric output jack

Fig. 603. *Simple one-tube converter permits use of broadcast receiver on shortwave bands.*

output of this circuit is 1500 kc. Accordingly, it can be applied to a broadcast receiver (home or car type) tuned to 1500 kc. The converter thus supplies the two input stages (first detector and oscillator) of a shortwave superhet, while the broadcast receiver furnishes the remaining stages. To obtain superhet action, the oscillator section of the converter (L3, L4 and C3) always operates at a frequency 1500 kc higher than that of the incoming signal.

The converter covers the frequency range 1.7 to 37 mc in three plug-in coil ranges: 1.7–4.8, 4–13 and 11–37 mc. Oscillator and antenna coils are changed together for each range. However, an individual builder can construct a coil-switching unit, if preferred, in lieu of plug-in coils.

Table H—SUPERHET CONVERTER COILS

1.7–4.8 mc
L1—66 turns No. 28 enameled wire on 1-inch-diameter form spaced to 1-inch
L2—10 turns No. 28 enameled wire closewound 1/16 inch from ground end of L1
L3—30 turns No. 22 enameled wire on 1-inch-diameter form spaced to 1 inch
L4—5 turns No. 22 enameled wire closewound 1/16 inch from ground end of L3

4–13 mc
L1—24 turns No. 22 enameled wire on 1-inch-diameter form spaced to 1 inch
L2—5 turns No. 22 enameled wire closewound 1/16 inch from ground end of L1
L3—16 turns No. 22 enameled wire on 1-inch-diameter form spaced to 3/4 inch
L4—4 turns No. 22 enameled wire closewound 1/16 inch from ground end of L3

11–37 mc
L1—$8\frac{1}{2}$ turns No. 22 enameled wire on 1-inch-diameter form spaced to 3/4 inch
L2—$2\frac{1}{2}$ turns No. 22 enameled wire closewound 1/16 inch from ground end of L1
L3—$6\frac{1}{2}$ turns No. 22 enameled wire on 1-inch-diameter form spaced to 5/8 inch
L4—3 turns No. 22 enameled wire closewound 1/16 inch from ground end of L3

The only required adjustment procedure is to set the ganged tuning capacitor (C1–C3) to its high-frequency (minimum-capacitance) position with coils for the lowest frequency band inserted. Adjust the trimmer of transformer T for peak signal output from the receiver (tuned to 1500 kc) when a 1.7-mc signal is applied to the converter ANTENNA INPUT terminals. This signal may be obtained from an AM signal generator.

The converter is designed for the reception of radiophone and other modulated signals only. To render CW signals audible, a beat oscillator must be fed into the second detector of the broadcast receiver. This oscillator must be tunable from a few thousand cycles above to a few thousand cycles below the receiver intermediate frequency (usually 455 kc).

The coils are wound on 1-inch diameter four-pin forms according to the specifications given in the coil table. A separate dial scale or calibration curve will be required for each coil range since the frequency ranges are not exact multiples of each other.

The converter is coupled to the receiver by means of transformer T. This is a manufactured component which is equipped with a trimmer capacitor for setting to the receiver frequency.

Power supply requirements of the converter are: 11 to 12 ma at 250 volts dc; 0.3 ampere at 6.3 volts ac or dc.

Portable transceiver

A transceiver provides a complete station in a small enclosure. Therefore it is handy and extremely portable when battery-operated. The use of transceivers in the crowded high-frequency bands is not encouraged at present, however, because there is a tendency for these units to radiate interference when used for reception.

Its small size enables the transceiver to be built completely in the form of a midget unit like the *walkie-talkie* or *handie-talkie,* and these very portable arrangements are invaluable for emergency work as in civilian defense on-spot communications. These applications would make it worth while to keep a set of ready-to-operate transceivers on hand for emergencies.

In the transceiver circuit shown in Fig. 604, the right-hand triode section of the 3A5 tube operates as a 2-meter oscillator when transmitting and as a 2-meter superregenerative detector when receiving. The left triode section operates as a headphone amplifier when receiving and as a microphone amplifier–modulator when transmitting. A three-pole two-position switch (S1-a,

S1-b and S1-c changes the circuit over from TRANSMIT to RECEIVE. A single-button carbon microphone is used.

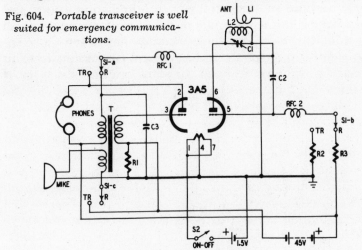

Fig. 604. *Portable transceiver is well suited for emergency communications.*

PORTABLE TRANSCEIVER (Fig. 604)

Resistors: R1—470 ohms; R2—22,000 ohms; R3—10 megohms
Capacitors: C1—25-μμf midget variable; C2 —50-μμf 500-volt mica; C3—.005-μf 500-volt mica
Coils: L1 —1 turn No. 16 enameled wire ½ inch in diameter mounted near grid end of L2; L2—4½ turns No. 16 enameled wire airwound ½ inch in diameter and spaced to ½ inch; RFC1, RFC2—1.8-μh rf chokes (IRC-CLA)
Transformer: T—transceiver (Triad A-21X or equivalent)
Tube: 3A5
Socket: octal
Miscellaneous: S1-a, S1-b, S1-c—3-pole 2-position wafer switch; S2—spst toggle switch; 2,000-ohm magnetic phones; single-button carbon mike; 45-volt battery pack; 1½-volt cell

Power is furnished by one 1-½ and one 45-volt battery. Somewhat higher transmitter power may be obtained with higher B-battery voltages (up to 90 volts) but the radiation while receiving will be proportionately objectionable.

The antenna may consist of a whip or rod attached to the transceiver case by insulators and connected to the *hot* end of the pickup coil L1.

Wired-radio transmitter

Wired-radio (carrier-current) communication uses the power lines to carry the radio signals from transmitter to receiver. This form of communication is attractive to many experimenters since no FCC license is required; and if the transmitter power is kept low, no radio interference is created.

Wired radio is most efficient at very low radio frequencies. The distance covered depends upon many factors such as the number

111

of appliances or machines operating on the line; the distance between transmitter and receiver along the wires; whether the power lines are overhead or underground, etc. Both transmitter and receiver must be on the same side of the distribution transformer since it is difficult for a low-powered transmitter to force a radio-frequency signal through a transformer and best results seem to be obtained with overhead lines. In some localities, distances of

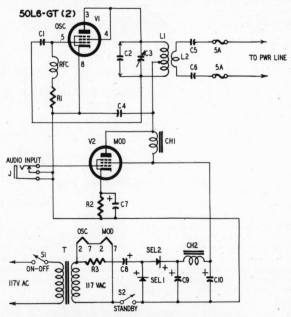

WIRED-RADIO TRANSMITTER (Fig. 605)

Resistors: R1—50,000 ohms, 10 watts; R2—180 ohms, 2 watts; R3—4.7 ohms, 2 watts
Capacitors: C1, C4—100-μμf 500-volt mica; C2—2,500 volts (see text); C3—150-μμf variable; C5, C6—0.1-μf 600-volt oil; C7—25-μf 25-volt electrolytic; C8, C9, C10—40-μf 450-volt electrolytic
Coils: L1—185 turns No. 22 enameled wire closewound on 1½-inch-diameter form and tapped at 60th turn from grid end; L2—10 turns No. 20 dcc wire wound over center of L1 and insulated from it with a double layer

of Scotch tape; RFC—80-mh rf choke (Meissner 19-5596 or equivalent); CH1, CH2—175-ma 10-h filter chokes (UTC S-29 or equivalent)
Transformer: T—1:1 isolation (Stancor P-6160 or equivalent)
Tubes: V1, V2—50L6-GT; SEL1, SEL2—150-ma selenium rectifiers
Sockets: octal (2)
Miscellaneous: S1, S2—spst toggle switches; J—closed-circuit midget phone jack; 5-amp fuses (2)

Fig. 605. *Wired-radio transmitter makes use of power lines to carry radio signals.*

several line miles can be covered easily while in other places one or two city blocks appear to be the limit. Wired-radio communication can be carried on between a group of experimenters with each assigned to a particular frequency.

The wired-radio transmitter shown in Fig. 605 will operate on frequencies between 110 and 475 kc. The rf oscillator is a triode-connected 50L6-GT in a Hartley circuit. A second 50L6-GT, pentode-connected, is the modulator. A carbon microphone with 3 to 6 volts dc and a microphone type coupling transformer will operate this modulator directly. Crystal and dynamic microphones require speech amplification. The amplifier must have a minimum audio output of 5.7 volts rms. Both oscillator and modulator receive dc power from a selenium type voltage doubler. The isolating transformer T is included for safety.

The main frequency-determining capacitor is C2. The variable capacitor C3 is only a trimmer. Various values of C2 may be plugged in for different frequencies. The following list shows frequencies which may be secured with typical standard capacitances:

Value of C2	Frequency (C3 set at mid-range)
7,000 $\mu\mu$f	110 kc
3,000 "	165 "
2,000 "	200 "
1,500 "	260 "
800 "	320 "
500 "	400 "
370 "	475 "

Rf output is coupled to the power line by the low-impedance pickup coil L2 and the high-voltage isolating capacitors C5 and C6. These connections must be made at the service box, as close as possible to the point at which the line enters the building.

Wired-radio receiver

Fig. 606 is the circuit of a wired-radio receiver which serves as a companion unit to the transmitter described in the previous section. This is a regenerative receiver giving loudspeaker operation. Its tuning range is 95 to 400 kc. Like the transmitter, the receiver must be coupled to the power line at a point as close as possible to the entrance of the line into the building—preferably at the meter or service box. Blocking capacitors C1 and C2 prevent short circuit of the line.

Details of the input coupler (L1–L2–L3) are given in Fig. 606. The basis of this unit is L2 which is one coil of a 455-kc if transformer. The second coil is removed from the transformer dowel and the largest pi from a National type R-152 transmitting rf choke is slipped over the dowel (as L3) and cemented to the top of L2. Starting ⅛ inch below L2, coil L1 (15 turns of No. 26 dcc wire) is wound around the dowel.

Regeneration control R2 should be adjusted for maximum sensitivity without receiver oscillation. If regeneration is not obtained readily, reverse the connections of L3. The standby switch S1 allows the receiver to be switched off during transmission without extinguishing the tube heaters.

Wired-radio intercom

The wired-radio transmitter (Fig. 605) and receiver (Fig. 606) may be combined to form a carrier-current type of intercommunication unit. A talk–listen switch can be arranged to switch the

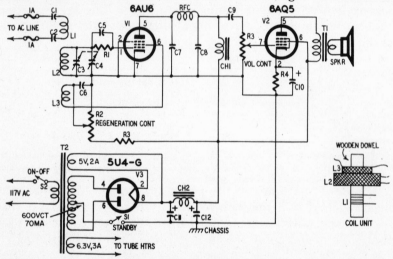

WIRED-RADIO RECEIVER (Fig. 606)

Resistors: R1—2.2 megohms; R2—25,000-ohm wirewound pot; R3—15,000 ohms, 1 watt; R4—500,000-ohm pot; R5—330 ohms, 2 watts

Capacitors: C1, C2—.1-μf 600-volt oil; C3, C4—dual 365-μμf midget variable, parallel sections; C5—250-μμf 500-volt mica; C6—.25-μf 400-volt tubular; C7, C8—500 μμf mica; C9—.05-μf, 400 volt; C10—25-μf 25-volt electrolytic; C11, C12—8-μf 600-volt electrolytics

Coils: L1, L2, L3—see text; RFC—60-mh rf choke (Meissner 19-5594 or equivalent)

Chokes: CH1—350-h af coupling (Thordarson 20C50); CH2—8-h 150-ma filter (Thordarson 20C54)

Transformers: T1—output, 8,500 ohms to voice coil; T2—300-0-300 volts, 70 ma; 5 volts, 2 amps; 6.3 volts, 3 amps (Thordarson 22R02 or equivalent)

Tubes: V1—6AU6; V2—6AQ5; V3—5U4-G

Sockets: octal; 7-pin miniature (2)

Miscellaneous: S1, S2—spst toggle switches; PM speaker; 1-amp fuses (2)

Fig. 606. *Wired-radio receiver to be used in conjunction with wired-radio transmitter of Fig. 605.*

transmitter on as it switches the receiver off and vice versa. This double-pole double-throw switch would replace both S2 in the transmitter and S1 in the receiver.

Transistorized intercom

Conventional junction transistors are employed in the inter-communicator shown in Fig. 607. Using three Sylvania type 2N34 units, the power output is 50 mw. While this power will not

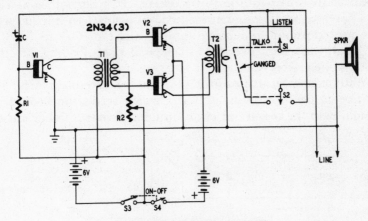

TRANSISTORIZED INTERCOM (Fig. 607)

Resistors: R1—100,000 ohms; R2—50,000-ohm wirewound pot

Capacitor: C—2-μf miniature electrolytic

Transformers: T1—Class-B driver, 10,000-ohm plate to push-pull grids (Thordarson T20D75 or equivalent). T2—output 4,000

ohms to 3.2-ohm voice coil (Thordarson TS-24S60 or equivalent)

Transistors: V1, V2, V3—2N34 (Sylvania)

Sockets: Transistor (3)

Miscellaneous: S1, S2—dpdt lever switch; S3, S4—dpst toggle switch; 3.2-ohm PM speaker; 6-volt batteries (2)

Fig. 607. *Simple intercom uses three transistors.*

produce a large amount of volume, it is sufficient for small offices and an average quiet home.

The unit comprises one single-ended voltage amplifier and a push-pull power-output stage. In the TALK position of changeover switch S1–S2, the small loudspeaker serves as a dynamic microphone. Potentiometer R2 is preset for a total collector current of 8 to 10 ma in the output stage.

Dc power is furnished by two 6-volt batteries. Good life may be obtained with jumbo-size flashlight cells such as Eveready No. 950, size D (four cells to each 6-volt battery). Being self-powered, this intercom is adaptable to portable and line-free operation.

A two-wire line can be used, as shown in Fig. 607, or a single line and ground. An identical intercom is assumed to be connected at the other end of the line.

Pocket emergency crystal receiver

The chief attraction of crystal receivers is their ability to operate without power supplies. New attention is focused on the crystal set as an emergency receiver for use during power blackouts.

Fig. 608 shows the circuit of a crystal set which can be built small enough to fit into a shirt pocket. It need not be as large as a hearing aid. The slug-tuned coil in parallel with a 20-$\mu\mu$f silver-mica capacitor provides a tuning range of 500 to 1600 kc, although the exact coverage will depend upon loading effects of the antenna used.

With strong local broadcast stations, the antenna can be 6 to 10 feet of flexible insulated wire thrown across the floor, hung from a door, or tossed out of an upstairs window. Other satisfac-

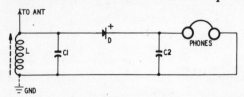

Fig. 608. *Crystal receiver uses a minimum number of parts.*

POCKET EMERGENCY CRYSTAL RECEIVER (Fig. 608)

Capacitors: C1—20-$\mu\mu$f 500-volt silver mica; C2—.002-μf 500-volt mica
Coil: L—.5–5-mh slug-tuned (Miller 6316 or equivalent)
Detector: D—1N56 crystal diode
Phones: 2,000-ohm magnetic

tory emergency antennas are bedsprings, electric chandeliers, window screens and screen doors. A good ground often will increase the volume of signals considerably.

Tuning is simply a matter of screwing the slug in and out of

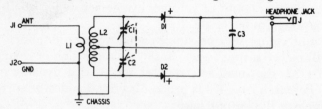

PUSH-PULL CRYSTAL RECEIVER (Fig. 609)

Capacitors: C1, C2—dual 365-$\mu\mu$f variable; C3—800-$\mu\mu$f mica
Coils: L1—46 turns No. 28 enameled wire closewound on layer of cellophane tape over exact center of L2; L2—220 turns No. 28 enameled wire closewound on 1½-inch diameter fiber tube and tapped at 110th turn
Detectors: D1, D2—1N54 crystal diodes
Miscellaneous: J—midget open-circuit phone jack; J1, J2—terminal connectors

Fig. 609. *Crystal receiver using two crystal diodes in a push-pull circuit.*

the coil. With a little practice, you will learn how far the screw must move to tune in a particular station.

Push-pull crystal receiver

Fig. 609 shows a larger-sized crystal set employing two diodes in a full-wave circuit. Each half of the secondary winding (L2 of the rf input transformer) is separately tuned by one section of the 365-$\mu\mu$f two-gang variable capacitor C1–C2. This circuit has higher output than single-diode types. The type 1N54 germanium diodes give high efficiency as detectors in this circuit. They must be connected exactly as shown in Fig. 609.

The transformer L1–L2 is wound with No. 28 enameled wire on a four-inch length of bakelite, fiber or polystyrene tubing having a 1-1/2-inch diameter. It is not advisable to use cardboard tubing unless it has been impregnated with a good-grade insulating varnish and baked dry.

Heterodyne eliminator

Fig. 610 shows the circuit of a useful accessory for communications receivers. This unit is a heterodyne remover for phone reception. It may be plugged into the headphone jack of the receiver, the headphones then being connected to its AUDIO OUTPUT

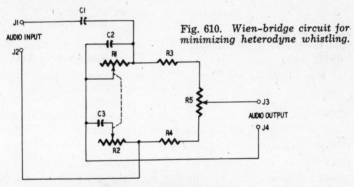

Fig. 610. *Wien-bridge circuit for minimizing heterodyne whistling.*

HETERODYNE ELIMINATOR (Fig. 610)

Resistors: R1, R2—dual 500,000-ohm pot; R3 —1,000 ohms; R4—2,200 ohms; R5—2,000- ohm wirewound pot

Capacitors: C1—.1-μf 400-volt mica; C2, C3— .0071-μf mica (.007 and .0001-μf in parallel) Miscellaneous: J1, J2, J3, J4—terminal connectors

terminals. Or it may be inserted between the first and second stages of the receiver, provided an interstage transformer is used at either the input or output of the eliminator.

In operation, the ganged potentiometer R1–R2 is adjusted to tune out the disturbing heterodyne whistle. If complete elimination does not result, potentiometer R5 then may be adjusted to make the rejection complete.

The circuit used is that of the Wien bridge, a null network. The operation of this circuit was described in Chapter 3 (Fig. 310). The tuning range of the eliminator is 40 to 9000 cycles, which means that this device will reject any frequency to which it is tuned within that range.

External S-meters

The less-expensive amateur superhet receivers are not equipped with intensity (S) meters. An external meter must be used with these sets when accurate indications of the strength of received

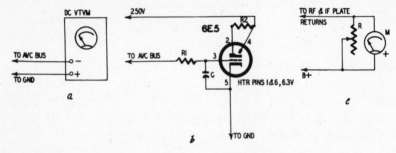

SIMPLE EXTERNAL S-METERS (Fig. 611)

(b)
Resistors: R1, R2—1 megohm
Capacitor: C—.001-μf 500-volt mica
Tube: 6E5

Socket: 6 pins
(c)
Resistor: R—15-ohm wirewound pot
Meter: M—0-1-ma dc

Figs. 611-a, -b, -c. *Three techniques for providing communications receivers with S-meters.*

signals are desired. Fig. 611 shows three such meter arrangements.

Since many experimenters own dc vacuum-tube voltmeters, a scheme is shown in Fig. 611-a for using a meter of this type temporarily as an S-indicator. The meter is connected between ground and the avc bus in the receiver. A pair of insulated pin jacks or binding posts may be installed in the receiver to accommodate the meter. The received signal sets up a negative avc bias voltage proportional to the signal strength, and this bias deflects the meter. Since the dc vacuum-tube voltmeter has very high input resistance, its connection into the circuit in this manner will not interfere with proper operation of the receiver.

Fig. 611-b shows a visual indicator of the electron-eye tube type. Operating voltages for the 6E5 tube are obtained from the receiver. A shielded six-wire cable may be used for connections between the electron-eye tube circuit and the receiver. The dc signal leads from the 6E5 are connected to ground and the avc bus in the same manner as the vacuum-tube voltmeter in the preceding example. The received signal, through the avc bias voltage, tends to close the eye shadow, the amount of closure being proportional to the signal strength.

Fig. 611-c shows a shunted dc milliammeter which is wired in series with the B-plus (plate-return) lead of one or more of the rf or if stages in the receiver. This meter operates on the change of plate current resulting from the avc action. Since the plate current *decreases* under the influence of avc action, the meter will deflect downward to indicate signal strength. The meter accordingly must be set initially to full scale in the absence of signals, by adjustment of the shunt rheostat.

Simple diode type noise clipper

Fig. 612 shows the circuit of another useful accessory for amateur communications receivers not equipped with internal noise-suppressor circuitry. The clipper may be connected to the

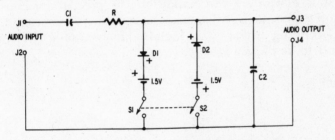

SIMPLE DIODE-TYPE AUDIO NOISE CLIPPER (Fig. 612)

Resistor: R—22,000 ohms

Capacitors: C1—.1-μf 400-volt tubular; C2—.007-μf mica

Diodes: D1, D2—1N34 crystals
Miscellaneous: S1, S2—dpst toggle switch; J1, J2, J3, J4—terminal connectors; 1½-volt batteries (2)

Fig. 612. *Audio clipper removes positive and negative peaks of noise pulses.*

receiver headphone jack and the headphones transferred to the AUDIO OUTPUT terminals; or the clipper may be inserted between the first and second audio stages of the receiver.

In operation, one diode leg clips the positive peak from noisy af signals; the other diode leg clips the negative peak. The total result is material softening of the harsh noise effects.

When the clipper is not in use, the dpst switch S1–S2 is opened to prevent drain of the 1-1½ volt cells through the back resistance of the diodes. The cells may be of the penlight variety or, for extra long life, mercury cells.

Curbing unauthorized radiation

An FCC license is required for every radio station as defined by Federal Law. In addition, the operator must hold a valid radio operator's license issued by the Federal Communications Commission, except that a *licensed* transmitter may be operated in the Citizen's band by an unlicensed person. The government of the country in which a radio station is operated has jurisdiction over the station and operator.

No licenses are required for certain short-range communication devices such as wireless microphones, wireless record players, and metal locators, provided the low-power signals emitted by these transmitters are kept within the intensity limit specified by the FCC. The legal operating distance is not very many feet from the transmitting antenna unless the frequency is quite low. The intensity of the signal may be measured satisfactorily only with a calibrated field strength meter. Unlicensed transmitters falling within legal limits must also be operated at low frequencies because it is difficult, if not impossible, to prevent long-distance radiation when high frequencies are used. Furthermore, the lawful operating distance for a high-frequency transmitter often is too short to be of value.

control devices

ONE of the most fascinating aspects of electronics always has been the art of remote control. This is the control of distant devices by means of radio signals. Here is real scientific magic! A closely allied art is that of electronic timing. Operations may be timed very precisely or time intervals measured very closely without any of the common mechanical clockwork devices. Electronics does this job accurately and quietly.

The circuits given in this chapter may be adapted to a variety of remote-control operations such as garage-door opening, model-airplane control, opening and closing distant locks, sounding alarms, and similar applications.

Capacitance-operated relay

Operation of this type of relay results from the nearness of objects. Approach its antenna and the relay closes. Move away and it opens. The capacitance-operated relay often is used in a store window as a "crowd stopper." With an antenna disc mounted inside the glass, lights can be made to flash on or an animated exhibit set into motion when a bystander places his hand or finger in front of the disc. The capacitance-operated relay also is used occasionally as an intrusion (burglar) alarm.

Fig. 701 shows the circuit of a simple capacitance relay. Here, a 50B5 tube is used as an rf oscillator and a 2050 as the relay tube. A manufactured capacitance relay coil assembly (Miller

No. 695) includes inductor L, rf choke RFC and trimmer capacitor C3. Dc voltage for the plate and screen of the 50B5 is supplied by the selenium rectifier and filter capacitor C1.

A pickup antenna is coupled to the oscillator through capacitor C4. This antenna may consist of a few feet of plain, insulated wire or it may be a metallic disc or plate. In some applications, a wire has been run around a door frame to detect the entry of

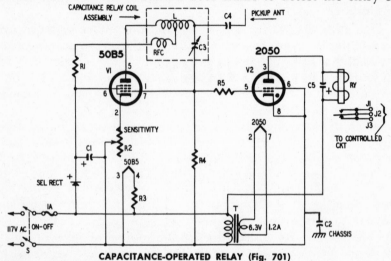

CAPACITANCE-OPERATED RELAY (Fig. 701)

Resistors: R1—3,300 ohms, 1 watt; R2—1,000-ohm wirewound pot; R3—433 ohms, 20 watts (500-ohm adjustable with slider set at 433 ohms); R4—680,000 ohms; R5—2.2 megohms

Capacitors: C1—40-μf 150-volt electrolytic; C2, C4—.1-μf 600-volt tubular; C5—10-μf 150-volt electrolytic

Coil: L—capacitance-relay coil assembly Miller No. 695 (C3 and RFC contained in unit)

Transformer: T—6.3-volt 1.2-amp filament (Triad F-14X or equivalent)

Tubes: V1—50B5; V2—2050; SEL—100-ma selenium rectifier

Sockets: octal; 7-pin miniature

Relay: RY—110 volts ac (Advance K1501-S or equivalent)

Miscellaneous: S—dpst toggle switch; J1, J2, J3—terminal connectors; 1-amp fuse

Fig. 701. *The presence of an object near the antenna will operate the relay. The relay tube is a thyratron.*

persons. In another intrusion-detector application, the antenna has consisted of a large metallic plate concealed under a rug inside a doorway.

Body capacitance, due to proximity to the antenna, alters the oscillator capacitance and the presence or strength of oscillation. This, in turn, changes the dc bias on the grid of the 2050 gas tube, causing this tube to fire and close the relay. Since the 2050 is ac-operated, it will extinguish and open the relay as soon as the object withdraws and the grid bias shifts back to its original value.

The sensitivity of the circuit depends upon the settings of C3 and R2. If the circuit is too sensitive, it will fall into a hair-trigger type of self-operation. If not sensitive enough, it will respond only to large objects or those in actual contact with the antenna. A compromise must be made between the adjustments of C3 and R2 to give a good combination of sensitivity and reliability.

Phototimer

Fig. 702 is the circuit of a simple electronic timer intended for controlling the lamp in a photographic enlarger or printing box but useful also for other timing purposes. It has a range of 5 to 50 seconds, depending upon the setting of potentiometer R1, but can be modified for longer intervals by increasing the resistance of R1, the capacitance of C1, or both.

When the instrument is first plugged into the power outlet, but with the operating switch S open, the 2D21 cathode heats and sets up a cathode–grid electron current. This current charges capacitor C1 with its upper terminal negative. When operating

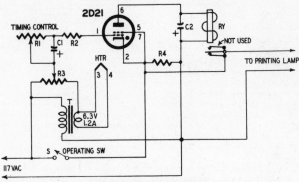

PHOTO TIMER (Fig. 702)

Resistors: R1—500,000-ohm pot; R2—47,000 ohms, 1 watt; R3—5,000 ohm pot, 10 watts; R4—47,000 ohms, 2 watts	(Triad F-14X or equivalent)
	Tube: 2D21
	Socket: 7-pin miniature
Capacitors: C1—100-μf 150-volt electrolytic; C2—10-μf 150-volt electrolytic	**Relay:** RY—110 volts ac (Advance K1501-S or equivalent)
Transformer: T—6.3-volt 1.2-amp filament	**Miscellaneous:** S—spst toggle switch

Fig. 702. *Simple electronic timer for work in photography.*

switch S is closed, 115 volts ac is applied to the printing lamp through the lower contact of the relay. The tube cannot conduct plate current because its grid is held at cutoff by the negative bias on capacitor C1. This charge eventually leaks off, however, through R1, at a rate determined by the time constant R1C1, thereby reducing the 2D21 grid bias. When the charge has fallen to a sufficiently low level, the 2D21 grid no longer is at cutoff potential and the tube conducts, closing the relay. This interrupts the ac voltage to the printing lamp and the latter is extinguished.

The slider on resistor R3 is set so that the maximum time interval occurs with R1 set to its maximum resistance.

Diode-type carrier-control relay

Fig. 703 shows the circuit of a simple carrier-control (wired-radio) relay which is operated by rf signals transmitted over the power line. The advantage of the diode type circuit is its ability to stand by without drawing any power.

The tuned circuit is a revamped 175-kc miniature if transformer (Miller No. 012-K-4). This transformer has two coils and two screwdriver-adjusted trimmer capacitors (C2 and C3). One capacitor (C3) is left intact across the coil, as shown, while the

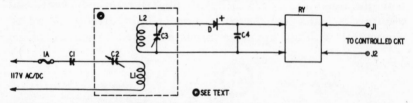

DIODE-TYPE CARRIER-CONTROL RELAY (Fig. 703)

Capacitors: C1—.01-μf 500-volt mica; C4— .002-μf 600-volt tubular	**Diode:** D—1N56 germanium crystal
	Relay: RY—Barber-Coleman AYLZ-2542S
Transformer: L1, L2, C2, C3—175-kc if Miller 012-K-4 or equivalent	**Miscellaneous:** J1, J2—terminal connectors; 1-amp fuse

Fig. 703. *Wired–radio relay is operated by signals transmitted through the power line.*

other (C2) is reconnected in series with its coil. This allows the primary (input) circuit to be series-tuned and the secondary to be parallel-tuned.

The signal is picked up from the line through blocking capacitor C1. The input circuit has a high impedance to the 60-cycle line frequency, but low impedance at the 175-kc control frequency.

The 1N56 germanium diode (D) is a high-conduction type which delivers increased dc output for a given rf input. Its rectification efficiency is excellent at 175 kc. The Micropositioner type of sensitive dc relay closes on 150 millivolts (0.7 ma dc). This level of only 105 microwatts insures positive action with a small rf control signal.

The circuit is tuned up initially by applying a 175-kc signal (from a signal generator or the control transmitter), substituting temporarily a dc microammeter for the relay and adjusting C2 and C3 for maximum deflection of the meter. Final tuning (a touching-up process) is accomplished with the receiver circuit picking up the transmitter signal from the power line.

This relay circuit is used in conjunction with the transmitter described immediately following and can be employed to sound an alarm, switch on lights and do similar tasks at distances with the power line as the only connecting medium. It has operated reliably at various points throughout a city block, as well as in the same house with the transmitter.

Carrier-control transmitter

Fig. 704 shows the circuit of a small 175-kc wired-radio transmitter for use with the carrier-current relay just described.

A triode-connected 50C5 is used as the oscillator. Dc power is supplied by the selenium rectifier and filter capacitor C4. The

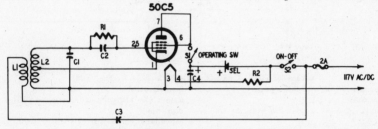

CARRIER-CONTROL TRANSMITTER (Fig. 704)

Resistors: R1—12,000 ohms, 2 watts; R2—433 ohms, 20 watts (500 ohms adjustable with slider set at 433 ohms)
Capacitors: C1—800-μμf 500-volt mica; C2—150-μμf 500-volt mica; C3—.1-μf 600-volt tubular; C4—40-μf 250-volt electrolytic
Coils: L1—10 turns No. 18 plastic insulated wire, wound around L2. L2—1-mh 300-ma rf choke tapped between first and second pi's (National R-300-U or equivalent)
Tube: 50C5; SEL—150-ma selenium rectifier
Socket: 7-pin miniature
Miscellaneous: S1, S2—spst toggle switches; 2-amp fuse

Fig. 704. *Wired–radio transmitter for use with the relay shown in Fig. 703.*

oscillator coil L2 is a pi wound 1-millihenry rf choke with a cathode tap taken between the first and second pies. The output coupling coil L1 consists of 10 turns of No. 18 plastic- or rubber-insulated wire wound tightly around L2. With the 800-μμf value given for capacitor C1, the resonant frequency will be approximately 175 kc. The actual frequency value is unimportant since the receiver can be tuned closely to the transmitter.

A signal is transmitted over the power line (through L1 and C3) each time the operating switch S1 is closed.

Gaseous-tube carrier-control relay

Fig. 705 shows a somewhat different type of wired-radio relay. Although this receiver circuit does not have the zero standby current characteristic of the one described in Fig. 703, it is preferred by some experimenters because it uses a more rugged, less expensive relay. This circuit is tuned to the frequency of the incoming signal by slug-tuned coil L (0.5–5 mh) and capacitor C in series. This gives a tuning range of 50–160 kc with C having a value of .002 μf, and 72–225 kc with C as .001 μf.

The voltage divider R1-R2 maintains the starter anode (pin 7) of the OA4–G tube at a voltage slightly less than that required to fire the tube. When an rf signal is received at the frequency to which LC is tuned, the resonant capacitor voltage increases

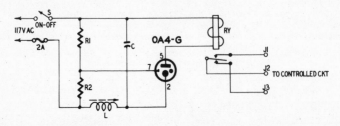

GASEOUS-TUBE CARRIER-CONTROL RELAY (Fig. 705)

Resistors: R1, R2—15,000 ohms
Capacitor: see text
Coil: L—.5–5-mh adjustable inductor (Miller No. 6313 or equivalent)
Tube: OA4-G
Socket: octal
Relay: RY—110 volts ac (Advance K1501-S or equivalent)
Miscellaneous: S—spst switch; J1, J2, J3—terminal connectors; 2-amp fuse

Fig. 705. *Wired-radio relay circuit.*

the voltage between the cathode (pin 2) and starter anode (pin 7). This starts a discharge between the cathode and starter anode, releasing free ions which cause the discharge to transfer to the main anode (pin 5). The flow of anode current then closes the relay. When the signal ceases, the main discharge ends in the tube, since the latter is ac-supplied, and the relay opens.

Rf carrier-operated alarm

Fig. 706 is the circuit of an rf carrier-operated relay which may be used either to sound an alarm or operate a recorder when a carrier comes on the air or goes off. The control signal is picked up from the air by a rod or whip antenna or a short antenna wire. The tuned circuit L–C1 is resonant at the transmitter frequency. The carrier signal is rectified by the 1N56 germanium diode.

This is a high-current type of detector. The diode dc output closes the relay.

The sensitive dc relay is a Micropositioner type which closes at 106.7 μw dc (970 mv, 110 μamp). This relay is of the spdt type and is used to actuate the alarm circuit.

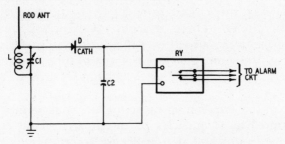

ON-AIR OR OFF-AIR RF-ACTUATED ALARM (Fig. 706)
Capacitors: C1—see text; C2—.002-μf mica Diode: 1N56 germanium crystal
Coil: L—see text Relay: RY—Barber-Coleman AYLZ-2542S

Fig. 706. *Rf carrier-operated alarm.*

However, by moving the lower stationary contact against the movable contact, with the relay in its resting position, the relay can be adapted to close the external circuit when the signal is interrupted. This is of use when it is necessary to monitor a broadcast transmitter.

Transistorized sensitive dc relay

Fig. 707 shows an amplifier-type of relay which will close on 17.5 microamperes dc input. This current may be obtained directly from a low-voltage dc source or from a rectifier of the crystal-diode type. A junction transistor is employed as the dc amplifier. The power supply is a single 1-1/2-volt cell. The dc relay is a Micropositioner type normally closing on 700 microamperes, 100 microwatts.

Since a steady collector current (comparable to the static plate current in a tube) flows in the transistor even when no input signal is applied, this current must be balanced out of the relay, otherwise the latter will be held closed by it. The bridge-type zero-set circuit, comprised of the two resistors and the potentiometer, are provided for this purpose. With no input signal, the potentiometer is set to open the relay (if it is closed) or to zero a low-resistance 0–100 dc microammeter connected temporarily in place of the relay (if the latter is open).

Model-airplane control receiver

The remote operation of mechanisms on board model airplanes in flight is one of the most attractive amateur applications of electronic control. Receivers have taken several characteristic forms. All have utilized the superregenerative circuit, when space was limited, since this circuit provides enormous sensitivity in spite of its simplicity. There is some preference, however, for the "hard" tube in this circuit over the short-lived gaseous tubes often used. Fig. 708 shows the circuit of a hard-tube receiver employing a triode-connected 3S4 and an 8,000-ohm sensitive dc relay (Sigma type 4F).

The coil L1 and tuning capacitor C1 values allow the receiver to be tuned to frequencies in the amateur 2-meter band. An amateur operator and station license accordingly is required for use of the transmitter. If the frequency of 27.255 mc is employed,

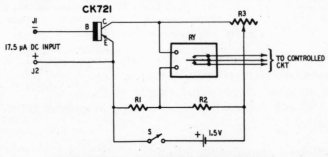

TRANSISTORIZED SENSITIVE DC RELAY (Fig. 707)

Resistors: R1, R2—500 ohms; R3—7,500 ohm wirewound pot

Transistor: CK721

Relay: Barber-Coleman AYLZ-2542S
Socket: Transistor
Miscellaneous: 1½-volt battery; S—spst toggle switch; J1, J2—terminal connectors

Fig. 707. *Amplifier type of relay using a junction transistor.*

an amateur license is not needed but special FCC permission must be obtained to use the transmitter which must be crystal-controlled. Because of this lower frequency, however, 27.255-mc operation requires longer antennas for maximum efficiency.

With no signal pickup, adjust potentiometer R2 until the relay closes. Then, back off the adjustment until the relay just opens. A signal then will close the relay. The signal is tuned in for maximum strength by adjustment of capacitor C1.

Model-airplane control transmitter

Transmitters for model-airplane control have varied designs, depending upon the amount of power output desired and, to some extent, upon the control frequency selected. Some model-control schemes employ modulated signals and others use plain carriers.

Fig. 709 shows a low-powered 1-tube 2-meter transmitter suitable for portable construction. The batteries can be self-contained

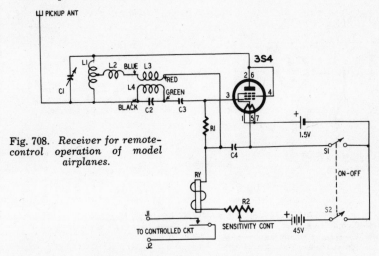

Fig. 708. *Receiver for remote-control operation of model airplanes.*

RECEIVER FOR MODEL-AIRPLANE CONTROL (Fig. 708)

Resistors: R1—3.3 megohms; R2—50,000-ohm pot

Capacitors: C1—3-30-μμf trimmer; C2—.002-μf 500-volt mica; C3—100-μμf 500-volt mica; C4—.005-μf 500-volt mica

Coils: L1—2 turns No. 14 enameled wire, airwound, ½-inch diameter, center tap; L2—.47-μh rf choke (IRC CLA); L3, L4—super-regeneration interruption-frequency coil (National OSR)

Tube: 3S4

Socket: 7-pin miniature

Relay: RY—8,000-ohm dc (Sigma 4F)

Miscellaneous: S1, S2—dpst toggle switch; J1, J2—terminal connectors; 45-volt battery; 1½-volt battery

in the transmitter case. This transmitter is usable with a sensitive receiver of the type shown in Fig. 708 for short-distance control purposes.

The characteristics of L and C1 have been chosen for operation in the amateur 2-meter band. An amateur operator and station license is therefore required.

In most instances, the antenna will be a vertical rod or whip. This should be as long as possible, with respect to one wavelength at the operating frequency. (In the middle of the 2-meter band, one wavelength is equal to 6.72 feet or approximately 80-¾ inches.)

The pushbutton switch S2 is arranged to interrupt the plate voltage so that a signal is sent out as long as the button is depressed.

Garage-door openers

Rf-operated garage-door openers have become very popular among experimenters and also with nontechnical motorists. These devices are based upon the simple principle of a control transmitter in the car operating a standby receiver in the garage to start

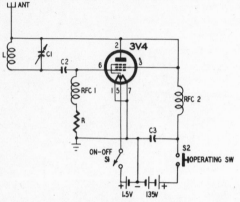

Fig. 709. *Transmitter for remote-control operation of model airplanes.*

TRANSMITTER FOR MODEL AIRPLANE CONTROL (Fig. 709)

Resistor: R—25,000 ohms

Capacitors: C1—15-μμf miniature variable; C2—75-μμf 500-volt mica; C3—.001-μf 500-volt mica

Coils: L—3 turns No. 14 enameled wire, air-wound, ⅝-inch diameter, spaced to ½ inch. RFC1—2.2-μh rf choke (IRC CLA); RFC2—1.8-

μh rf choke (IRC CLA)

Tube: 3V4

Socket: 7-pin miniature

Miscellaneous: S1—spst toggle switch; S2—spst normally open pushbutton switch; antenna (see text); 135-volt battery (two 67½-volt batteries in series); 1½-volt cell

the electric door-opening mechanism into motion. No uncommon circuitry is required in the electronic portion of this arrangement. In fact, any combination of control transmitter and receiver already described in this chapter might be employed. The model-airplane receiver (Fig. 708) and transmitter (Fig. 709), for example, could be used. A crystal-diode detector might be used in the receiver, instead of a tube, with a sensitive dc relay if the operator favors zero standby power. The scheme shown in Fig. 703 could be used, except that the diode would be connected to a high-frequency tuned circuit and antenna (chosen for the transmitter frequency) instead of the 175-kc transformer.

Most of the sensitive dc relays have relatively light contacts incapable of operating the door-opening motor directly. Hence, this relay must actuate a second relay for the heavy-duty circuit.

photoelectric devices

E LECTRONICS has made possible the control of various
devices by light beams. Electronics also has enabled us to
measure light intensities very conveniently.

The *photoelectric* circuits in this chapter include such electric-
eye devices as burglar (photoelectric intrusion) alarms, light controls (for switching lights on and off) and light meters, both with
and without tubes.

Tubeless light-controlled relay

Fig. 801 shows a photoelectric relay circuit which is adaptable
to any of the usual applications of light-operated relays: counting,
burglar alarm, door opening, light control, smoke detection, etc.
The advantage of this particular circuit is its complete freedom
from tubes and power supply. The initial expense of a sensitive
dc relay is amply compensated by the fact that this circuit draws
no standby power and has no tubes to be replaced.

The basis of the circuit is a high-output selenium self-generating
photocell (International Rectifier type DP-5). This cell, which
has an active exposed area of $2\frac{1}{4}$ square inches, generates sufficient
dc voltage when illuminated to actuate the relay directly.

The dc relay is a *Micropositioner* type which closes on 100 μw
(150 mv, 0.7 ma). The relay contacts may be set to close an
external circuit either on application or interruption of light, as
desired.

Phototube light-controlled relay

A type 930 phototube is the light-sensitive element in the photo-relay shown in Fig. 802. Illumination of this tube changes the grid bias of the 2D21 miniature thyratron, either firing this tube to close the relay or extinguishing it to open the relay. A rugged 117-volt ac relay is used.

In operation, illumination of the phototube develops a bias voltage across the 10-megohm resistor R. This bias cuts off

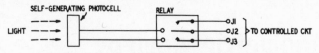

TUBELESS LIGHT-CONTROLLED RELAY (Fig. 801)

Photocell: International Rectifier DP-5   Miscellaneous: J1, J2, J3—terminal con-
Relay: RY—Barber-Coleman AYLZ-2542S   nectors

Fig. 801. *Photoelectric relay circuit.*

anode current in the 2D21 and the relay remains open. When the light beam is interrupted, the bias is reduced or removed, the 2D21 conducts and the relay closes.

For the anode and grid of the 2D21 to receive voltages of correct

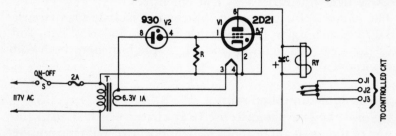

PHOTOTUBE LIGHT-CONTROLLED RELAY (Fig. 802)

Resistor: R—10 megohm, 1 watt   Sockets: 7-pin miniature; octal
Capacitor: C—8-μf 150-volt electrolytic   Relay: RY—117 volts ac (Advance K1501-S
Transformer: T—6.3-volt 1-amp filament   or equivalent)
(Stancor P6134 or equivalent)   Miscellaneous: S—spst toggle switch; 2-amp
Tubes: V1—2D21; V2—930   fuse (1); J1, J2, J3—terminal connectors

Fig. 802. *Photoelectric relay circuit using light-sensitive phototube.*

polarity, the 6.3-volt secondary winding of transformer T must be poled properly. If positive operation is not obtained, reverse the 6.3-volt leads.

Battery-operated high-sensitivity photorelay

In Fig. 803, a selenium type photocell is used as a photo-conductive device instead of employing its usual property as a self-generating cell. When this type of cell is dc-biased, it acts as a light-sensitive resistor and is capable of higher voltage output with a given amount of illumination than when used as a self-generating source.

Since the biased cell will have a voltage output even when darkened, due to its resistive nature, it has been incorporated into a four-arm bridge circuit for balancing this "dark voltage" to zero.

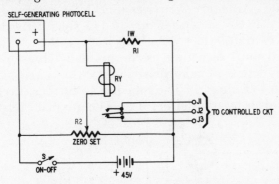

Fig. 803. *Photorelay circuit using a selenium type photocell.*

This balance is accomplished by adjusting the 10,000-ohm potentiometer R2 for zero dc voltage across the relay coil, with the cell darkened. Subsequent illumination then will unbalance the bridge and direct current will flow from the battery through the relay.

An 8,000-ohm 1.6-ma dc relay (Sigma type 4F) is employed. This relay can be adjusted for 1-ma response, if desired, by setting its pivot screw to reduce its spring tension. The relay contacts will handle 2 amperes at 117 volts ac.

The plus and minus symbols on the photocell (Fig. 803) indicate the polarity of the voltage delivered at these terminals when the cell operates as a self-generator. The negative battery terminal must be connected to the cell terminal designated positive in the schematic for low reverse-current flow.

Photoelectric intrusion (burglar) alarm

Fig. 804 shows an adaptation of the tube circuit previously shown in Fig. 802 to sound an alarm continuously after the light beam has been interrupted. The alarm, once set off, will continue to operate until the circuit is reset, even though the trespasser might step out of the beam.

This locked-in action is obtained by means of a double-pole double-throw 117-volt ac relay and the extra 6.3-volt transformer T2. When the light beam is interrupted, the 2D21 passes anode current and the relay closes. However, when armature A leaves contact 2, the circuit is broken between the power line and the 2D21 anode. Armature A arrives quickly at contact 1 and connects the relay coil independently to 117 volts derived from the secondary of transformer T2. This voltage then will hold the relay closed until such time as the normally closed pushbutton switch S2 is depressed momentarily to open the circuit and return armature A to contact 2. The tube has no further effect once the relay is held in by transformer T2. The auxiliary relay contacts

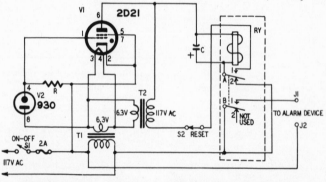

PHOTOELECTRIC INTRUSION (BURGLAR) ALARM (Fig. 804)

Resistor: R—10 megohms, 1 watt

Capacitor: C—8-μf 150-volt electrolytic

Transformers: T1, T2—6.3-volt 1-amp filament (Stancor P6134 or equivalent)

Tubes: V1—2D21; V2—930

Sockets: 7-pin miniature; octal

Relay: RY—117 volts ac dpdt (Potter & Brumfield MR11-A)

Miscellaneous: S1—spst switch; S2—pushbutton switch, normally closed; J1, J2—terminal connectors; 2-amp fuse

Fig. 804. *Interrupted light beam will set off this burglar alarm.*

(B and 1) energize the output terminals to supply 117 volts ac to the alarm device.

It is imperative that contact 1 be placed close to armature A so that the inertia of the armature can be depended on to carry it to contact 1. Otherwise, buzzer action will take place between armature A and contact 2.

Aside from the use of a dpdt relay and the second transformer T2 to obtain an isolated source of 117 volts, the circuit is the same as the one shown in Fig. 802. Remarks given earlier regarding operation of that circuit therefore apply also to this one.

Cadmium-selenide photocell relay

The cadmium-selenide crystal photocell provides high sensitivity in a miniature component. It also permits operation at high bias voltages.

Fig. 805 shows a cadmium-selenide photocell relay circuit which can be operated directly from the 117-volt power line without

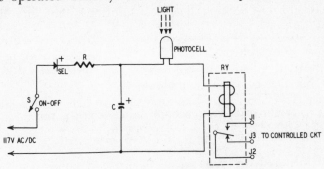

CADMIUM SELENIDE PHOTOCELL RELAY (Fig. 805)

Resistor: R—4.7 ohm, 1 watt

Capacitor: C—30-μf 150-volt electrolytic

Photocell: Clairex CL-3
Miscellaneous: S—spst switch; J1, J2, J3—
terminal connectors

.Fig. 805. *Photocell relay circuit using a cadmium-selenide unit.*

transformers. The small size of all components employed in this circuit permits the building of a complete relay in a small container. The dark current of the cadmium-selenide photocell is so low that the standby power drawn by the circuit during inactive periods will be tolerable.

Light meter with rugged milliammeter

Most light meters employ dc microammeters. These instruments are relatively delicate and expensive. An example is the common photographic exposure meter.

A more rugged 0–1 dc milliammeter can be used as the indicator by employing a high-output self-generating photocell. While the sensitivity will not be as great as with a microammeter, it will be adequate for most applications. Fig. 806 shows the circuit. A 50-ohm shunt rheostat is switched into the circuit in the HIGH illumination position of the range switch. This rheostat may be set to double the basic LOW range of the meter or to multiply it by some other desired factor.

When the range switch is set to the LOW range, full-scale deflection of the meter is obtained with 220 foot-candles of illumination.

Germanium photodiode light probe

Fig. 807 shows a simple circuit for the Sylvania type 1N77A subminiature photodiode as a self-generating light probe. This photodiode is extremely small and has a built-in lens. It can be mounted easily into the end of an exploring probe.

This light probe is useful for examining the illumination of surfaces and for checking density of solutions, films, etc. It is also

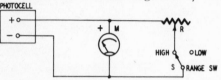

Fig. 806. *Circuit of light meter using high-output photocell.*

LIGHT METER USING RUGGED MILLIAMMETER (Fig. 806)

Resistor: R—50-ohm wirewound pot   Meter: M—0–1 ma dc
Photocell: International Rectifier DP-5   Switch: S—spdt

a good infra-red detector since the diode response peaks in the infra-red region of the spectrum. The meter will deflect when the cell is pointed toward a nearby warm body long before any visible glow can be seen.

The red dot on the shell of the 1N77A indicates the cathode

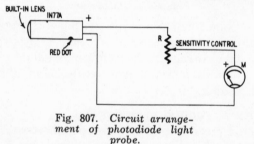

Fig. 807. *Circuit arrangement of photodiode light probe.*

lead which must be connected to the negative terminal of the meter in self-generating circuits like that of Fig. 807.

Biased germanium photodiode light probe

Where there is no objection to the use of a battery, the sensitivity of the light probe may be increased considerably by using the 1N77A photodiode as a light-sensitive resistor rather than a self-generating photocell. This arrangement is shown in Fig. 808.

In this circuit, the battery and diode are poled for reverse-current flow through the diode. With 7½ volts bias, as shown, full-scale deflection of the microammeter is obtained with lighting of approximately 600 lumens per square foot.

High-voltage-output light meter

Some applications require a higher dc output voltage for a given amount of illumination than is obtained directly from a self-generating photocell. It is common to employ dc amplifiers in such applications.

Fig. 809 shows a circuit which will give 10 volts or more, approximately 100 times the voltage output of the photocell alone.

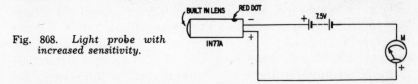

Fig. 808. *Light probe with increased sensitivity.*

The simplicity and stability of this circuit make it more desirable than the dc amplifier in many types of installations. This circuit is similar to the one given in Fig. 803, except that the relay in the latter circuit has been replaced by the dc output terminals in the present one. The cell constitutes one arm of a four-arm resistance

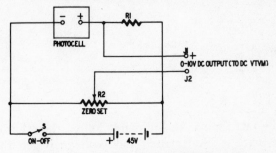

HIGH-VOLTAGE-OUTPUT LIGHT METER (Fig. 809)

Resistors: R1—47,000 ohms, 1 watt; R2—10,000-ohm wirewound pot

Photocell: International Rectifier DP-5

Miscellaneous: S—spst switch; J1, J2—terminal connectors; 45-volt battery

Fig. 809. *Light-meter circuit makes use of a resistance-bridge arrangement.*

bridge. With the cell darkened, this bridge is balanced by adjustment of the 10,000-ohm potentiometer R2 for zero output voltage. When the cell subsequently is illuminated, a dc voltage appears at the output terminals of the circuit and is proportional to the light intensity. Applied to a high-resistance load, such as a dc vacuum-tube voltmeter, this voltage reaches 10 or more with the circuit constants given.

The plus and minus symbols on the photocell (Fig. 809) indicate the polarity of the voltage delivered at these terminals when the cell is operated as a self-generator. The negative battery terminal must be connected to the positive cell terminal, as shown, for low reverse-current flow. If these connections are reversed, the cell will be forward-biased and may be damaged by the resulting high current flow.

Self-generating photocell made from selenium rectifier

An inexpensive but surprisingly effective self-generating photocell can be made from one plate removed from a small radio type (65–150-ma) selenium rectifier. The paint must be removed from the plate carefully with paint remover or lacquer thinner to permit light to reach the selenium-coated surface. This may be accomplished by dippings and light rubbing with a soft cloth. Be careful not to dig into the sprayed-metal front electrode which covers the selenium.

Pressure contact is made with the front and back of the plate, as shown in Fig. 810, by flat springs or lugs held into place firmly.

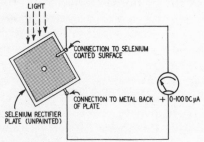

Fig. 810. *A self-generating photocell made from a selenium rectifier.*

Do not attempt to solder to the plate. When the selenium-coated face of the plate is illuminated, a dc voltage is generated. The selenium surface is negative and the back of the plate is positive.

Fig. 810 shows how the rectifier-plate photocell can be connected to a dc microammeter to form a light meter. The simple cell can be used also to actuate a sensitive dc relay in a circuit similar to the one given in Fig. 801. In addition to functioning as a self-generating photocell, the rectifier plate can be used also as a photoconductive element in the circuits shown in Figs. 803 and 809.

Photorelays in home-lighting control

Any of the photorelay circuits shown in this chapter can be used to switch lights on automatically when daylight drops to a level too dim for comfort or convenience. The light-sensing photocell or phototube of the relay circuit is installed in a part of the house or office which is most susceptible to changes in daylight. The circuit is arranged so that the relay contacts are held open as long as the photocell or phototube receives adequate light but are closed as soon as this light diminishes. In the circuits in Figs. 801, 802 and 805, for example, the lower relay contacts may be used.

The photorelay should be used to operate a second, heavy-duty, slave relay which will perform the actual switching of the lights.

Solar batteries

Combinations of self-generating photocells may be employed to supply dc operating power to electronic circuits of many types including transistorized radio receivers, flea-powered transmitters, phono oscillators, alarms, relays, door openers, automobile headlight dimmers, and intercoms. They may be used also to power non-transistorized, tubeless devices such as telegraphs, telephones, sensitive dc relays, alarms, or used as battery chargers and dielectric amplifiers.

A combination of cells operated from bright sunlight will deliver the maximum dc output possible with this arrangement. Somewhat less output is obtained with artificial illumination such as light from incandescent lamps. Silicon photocells deliver somewhat higher current than selenium units.

The term *solar battery* is used to describe a combination of photocells (and, in some instances, a single cell having high output). Single self-generating photocells may be connected in series for higher output voltage, in parallel for higher output current, or in series-parallel for greater current and voltage. The current or voltage increases approximately as the number of cells. Thus, two cells in series will deliver about twice the output voltage of one, if the cells are equally illuminated. Similarly, two cells in parallel deliver approximately twice the current supplied by one.

Photocell manufacturer's literature gives the important electrical and optical characteristics of individual units needed when considering the connection of these units into a solar battery. These characteristics show the various relations between light intensity, output current, output voltage and load resistance. The internal resistance of the solar battery increases as more cells are added in series, and decreases as cells are added in parallel.

When mounting cells in a solar battery arrangement, group them close together and keep their sensitive surfaces in the same plane. In this way there will be greater likelihood that each cell will receive the same illumination as its neighbor. When uncased cells are used they must be covered with a glass or transparent plastic plate for protection. This cover must be kept clean to insure maximum sensitivity to light.

Solar batteries provide excellent unattended service provided they are mounted so as to receive sunlight continuously during the operating period. When the battery must be operated throughout the day, some means must be provided for "following the sun." In an advanced setup, a servo system may be used to keep the battery pointed always toward the sun as it moves across the sky. When such a scheme is too complicated, a horizontal hemispherical surface might be studded with small cells so that a reasonable area of the photoelectric material is always under illumination. When neither of these schemes is feasible, the sun battery must be rotated by hand to track the sun.

miscellaneous circuits

THE circuits included in this chapter will be important to many electronic experimenters. But they did not seem to fit into the natural groupings provided by the first eight chapters of this book.

These are complete instruments and devices in themselves. They are not intended primarily for combination with other circuits.

One-tube stroboscope

The timed flashes of light from a stroboscope seemingly stop the motion of a moving machine. This makes possible the observation of bending, twisting or other distortion of parts while actually in motion. Play the flashing light on a revolving fan, for example, adjust the flashing to correspond to the speed of the machine and the blades stand still. Illuminate a spinning phonograph record and its rotation appears to stop, allowing wobble to be seen plainly.

Fig. 901 is a stroboscope circuit employing only one tube, the flashing *strobotron*. This tube, a Sylvania 1D21, operates in a relaxation oscillator circuit in which it performs the double role of oscillator gas tube and the source of light flashes. For concentration of light, the tube is mounted in front of a polished reflector. A photographic flash-gun reflector is satisfactory.

The flash rate is continuously variable from 10 per second (600 flashes per minute to 112 per second (6,720 per minute) by adjusting potentiometer R5.

Dc operating voltages are supplied by a selenium type voltage doubler composed of rectifiers SEL1 and SEL2, capacitors C1 and C2 and current-limiting resistors R1 and R2. The small isolation transformer T is included for safety.

The 1D21 tube plugs into a standard four-pin socket. This tube and its reflector may be attached to the end of a four-conductor

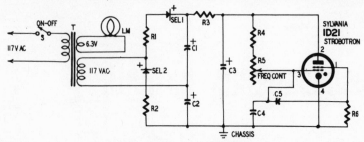

1-TUBE STROBOSCOPE (Fig. 901)

Resistors: R1, R2—10 ohms, 1 watt; R3—3,500 ohms, 10 watts; R4—47,000 ohms, 2 watts; R5—1-megohm pot; R6—2.2.-megohm pot

Capacitors: C1, C2—20-μf 450-volt electrolytic; C3—10-μf 600-volt electrolytic; C4—.1-μf 600-volt tubular; C5—.01-μf mica

Transformer: T—midget power (Merit P-3045 or equivalent)

Tube: 1D21 Strobotron; SEL1, SEL2—150-ma selenium rectifiers

Socket: 4-pin

Miscellaneous: S—spst toggle switch; LM—No. 47 pilot-lamp assembly

Fig. 901. *Single-tube stroboscope circuit.*

cable for holding close to the machine under observation or it may be mounted permanently to the front panel of the instrument case.

Simple Geiger counters

Fig. 902 shows two simple circuits for Geiger counters. The arrangement in Fig. 902-a uses no tubes in the circuit proper, only the Geiger tube for radiation pickup.

Polarizing voltage is supplied by the miniature 300-volt battery. The 1-megohm series isolating resistor R1 limits the current to a safe value. Each radioactive particle passing through the Geiger tube produces a click in the headphones. The intensity of radiation from a sample is judged by the number of clicks above the "background count" produced by cosmic rays and other local sources.

The amplifier tube in the second circuit (Fig. 902-b) provides louder clicks and somewhat better over-all sensitivity. For economy, three separate batteries should be used, as shown. A higher-voltage Geiger tube, such as type 1B85, can be used for increased sensitivity in this circuit by substituting a 900-volt battery for the 300-volt unit and a 1,600-volt coupling capacitor for the 600-volt capacitor.

The operator must employ more than ordinary caution when working on these circuits since the high-voltage batteries can deliver a nasty shock which, under the proper conditions, will be dangerous. *Be careful!*

Complete professional Geiger counter

Fig. 903 shows the circuit of a professional instrument employ-

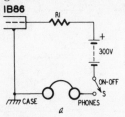

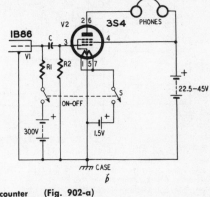

Figs. 902-a, -b. *Two Geiger-counter circuit arrangements. The one shown at the right is a more sensitive unit.*

Simple Geiger counter   (Fig. 902-a)

Resistor: R1—1 megohm

Tube: 1B86 Geiger

Single-tube circuit   (Fig. 902-b)

Resistors: R1, R2—1 megohm
Capacitor: C—.04-μf 600-volt tubular (see text)
Tubes: V1—1B86 Geiger (see text); V2—3S4

Switch: S—spst
Phones: 2,000-ohm magnetic
Battery: 300 volts
Socket: 7-pin miniature
Miscellaneous: Phones—2,000-ohm magnetic; 1½-volt battery; 45-volt battery; 300- or 900-volt battery (see text)

ing two amplifier stages and giving both headphone signals and a meter reading to indicate the strength of radioactivity.

A 1B86 tube is shown with a 300-volt energizing battery. For increased sensitivity, a higher-voltage tube such as type 1B85 may be used if the battery voltage is increased to 900, and capacitor C1 changed to a 1,000- or 1,600-volt type. In addition to battery high-voltage supply, the high dc voltage also may be obtained from dry-cell-operated vibrator type power supplies such as Victoreen type 517C or Precise Measurements Corp. model 10MVT.

The amplifier is designed to eliminate low frequencies. The setting of gain control R5 governs the meter deflection for a given radioactivity level. If accurate meter-scale multiplication is desired, a step type attenuator should be substituted for R5 for accurate resetting. The meter scale may be graduated in milliroentgens per hour with the aid of a number of ore samples and a standard Geiger counter for comparison. Somewhat less-sensitive response will be obtained with a plate-screen battery of 67½ volts.

Electronic metronome

Fig. 904 shows the circuit of a simple electronic metronome providing pulses or beats ranging from 1 every 2 seconds to 5 per

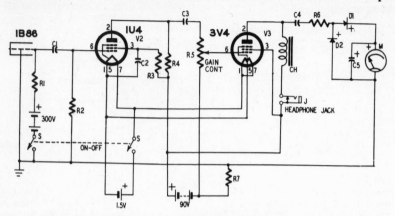

2-TUBE GEIGER COUNTER (Fig. 903)

Resistors: R1—5.1 megohms; R2, R4—1 megohm; R3—2.2 megohms; R5—3-megohm pot; R6—39,000 ohms; R7—470 ohms

Capacitors: C1—800-μμf 500-volt mica (see text); C2—.02-μf 400-volt tubular; C3—.001-μf mica; C4—.1-μf 400-volt tubular; C5—250-μf 15-volt electrolytic

Choke: CH—750 mh (Thordarson 20C58 or equivalent)

Tubes: V1—1B86 (see text); V2—1U4; V3—3V4

Diodes: D1, D2—1N34 crystals

Sockets: 7-pin miniature (2)

Miscellaneous: S—dpst toggle switch; M—0-50-μa dc meter; 1½-volt battery; 90-volt battery (see text); 300- or 900-volt battery (see text); J—phone jack

Fig. 903. *Circuit of Geiger counter using two stages of amplification.*

second. Made audible by a 4- or 5-inch loudspeaker, the volume of these pulses is set by means of potentiometer R3. The pulse rate is set by means of potentiometer R2, being slowest when R2 is at its high-resistance setting. This instrument may be used in the usual manner for setting the rhythm for music or for any of the other timing applications where an audible count is required.

The basis of the metronome is a low-frequency relaxation oscillator composed of the neon lamp NE, resistors R1 and R2 in series and capacitor C1. The neon lamp fires at a regular rate determined by the time constant of the R1–R2–C1 combination. Each firing delivers one pulse to the grid of the 6BF5 amplifier. This pulse then is amplified and made audible through the loudspeaker.

Operating power is supplied by a midget transformer T2 and a half-wave selenium rectifier dc circuit. Standby switch S2 allows the metronome to be silenced without extinguishing the tube heater or disturbing the volume control setting.

Treasure (metal) locator

The standard electronic locator for underground metal consists of a separate portable transmitter and receiver mounted on the same carrying frame. The transmitter sends an rf signal from its

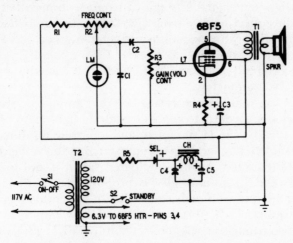

ELECTRONIC METRONOME (Fig. 904)

Resistors: R1—200,000 ohms, 1 watt; R2—2-megohm pot; R3—1-megohm pot; R4—200 ohms, 2 watts; R5—4.7 ohms, 1 watt

Capacitors: C1—1-μf 200-volt tubular; C2—.1-μf 200-volt tubular; C3—25-μf 25-volt electrolytic; C4, C5—dual 16-μf 250-volt electrolytic

Transformers: T1—output, 2,500 ohms to voice coil (Merit A-3025 or equivalent); T2—midget power transformer (Merit P-3045 or equivalent); CH—8-h 100-ma filter choke (Merit C-2995 or equivalent)

Tube: 6BF5; SEL—75-ma selenium rectifier

Socket: 7-pin miniature

Miscellaneous: S1, S2—spst toggle switches; LM—NE 48 neon lamp assembly; 3—4-ohm miniature PM speaker

Fig. 904. *Simple electronic metronome uses a low-frequency relaxation oscillator.*

loop antenna into the earth. If no metal is in the path of the radiated wave, the receiver loop antenna picks up no signal since it is positioned for zero direct pickup from the transmitter loop. But if metal is encountered, this mass will reflect a portion of the wave, which then will be picked up by the receiver to produce a headphone signal and deflect a meter. Thus, a loud signal and a pronounced deflection of the meter are obtained when the operator carries the locator over buried metal.

Fig. 905 shows the circuit of a metal locator of this type. The upper portion of the diagram is the 100-kc tuned rf receiver; the lower portion the crystal-controlled transmitter. The receiving loop antenna L1 is mounted horizontally (parallel to the earth's surface) and transmitting antenna L2 is vertical. This orientation

145

usually minimizes direct transmission between the two loops.

Both receiver and transmitter are fixed-tuned to the single frequency. The receiver is aligned initially by adjustment of loop trimmer C2 and the trimmers of the 100-kc if transformers T1 and T2. The alignment signal is obtained from the transmitter. First, tune the transmitter by adjusting C12 for maximum deflection of an rf vacuum-tube voltmeter connected temporarily across L2, then loop an insulated wire around L1 and L2 for coupling. Finally, vary the receiver adjustments C2, T1 and T2 for maximum deflection of the microammeter.

The receiver circuit contains two 100-kc rf amplifiers employing 1T4 pentodes, a diode detector and pentode first audio amplifier (both provided by the 1U5) and an audio output amplifier (3S4). The microammeter deflection is proportional to the strength of the received carrier wave. A tone-modulated signal is audible in the headphones and its volume also is proportional to the received signal. Headphone volume is controlled by potentiometer R3.

The transmitter is a 100-kc crystal oscillator employing a 3A5 tube with two triode sections connected in parallel. This oscillator is grid-modulated at approximately 400 cycles by the triode-connected 1U4 audio oscillator.

The transmitting and receiving antennas are identical. Specifications will be found in the parts list for this unit. The mounting frames may be made of plastic or of waterproofed wood. Each antenna should be mounted as close as possible to the circuit with which it is associated. Making the receiving antenna rotatable over a small angle, as shown in Fig. 906, will permit close adjustment for minimum direct pickup from the transmitter and maximum pickup from the metallic mass. In the interest of complete shielding, batteries B1 and B2 should be mounted inside the metal receiver case and batteries B3 and B4 inside the metal transmitter case.

Diode type field-strength meter

The field-strength meter is a necessary instrument in the adjustment of transmitting antennas and in making signal-strength surveys. It is invaluable also in monitoring radiophone signals, tracking interference and as a wavemeter.

The advantage of a diode type field-strength meter is its freedom from batteries or other types of local power supply. Although not as sensitive as a tube instrument, it can be used in any of the applications except signal-intensity surveys at points distant from the transmitter.

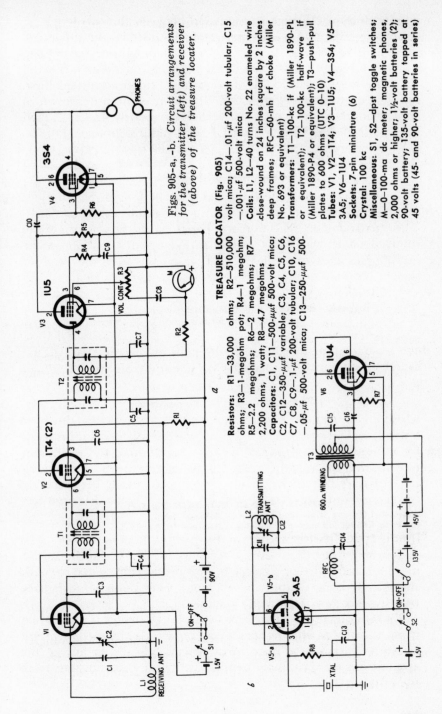

Figs. 905-a, -b. *Circuit arrangements for the transmitter (left) and receiver (above) of the treasure locater.*

TREASURE LOCATOR (Fig. 905)

Resistors: R1—33,000 ohms; R2—510,000 ohms; R3—1-megohm pot; R4—1 megohm; R5—2.2 megohms; R6—2 megohms; R7—2,200 ohms, 1 watt; R8—4.7 megohms

Capacitors: C1, C11—500-μμf 500-volt mica; C2, C12—350-μμf variable; C3, C4, C5, C6, C7, C8, C9—.1-μf 200-volt tubular; C10, C16—.05-μf 500-volt mica; C13—250-μμf 500-volt mica; C14—.01-μf 200-volt tubular; C15 —.001-μf 500-volt mica

Coils: L1, L2—40 turns No. 22 enameled wire close-wound on 24 inches square by 2 inches deep frames; RFC—60-mh rf choke (Miller No. 693 or equivalent)

Transformers: T1—100-kc if (Miller 1890-PL or equivalent); T2—100-kc half-wave if (Miller 1890-P4 or equivalent); T3—push-pull plates to 600 ohms (UTC 0-10)

Tubes: V1, V2—1T4; V3—1U5; V4—3S4; V5— 3A5; V6—1U4

Sockets: 7-pin miniature (6)

Crystal: 100 kc

Miscellaneous: S1, S2—dpst toggle switches; M—0-100-ma dc meter; magnetic phones, 2,000 ohms or higher; 1½-volt batteries (2); 90-volt battery; 135-volt battery tapped at 45 volts (45- and 90-volt batteries in series)

147

Fig. 907 shows the circuit of a diode type field-strength meter which covers the frequency range of 800 kc to 150 mc and utilizes

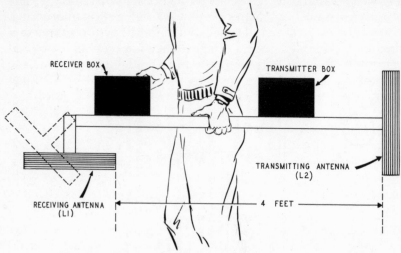

Fig. 906. *Receiving and transmitting antennas for the treasure locator.*

four separate plug-in coils. All the coils are wound on 1-inch-diameter 4-pin forms (Millen 45004). The coil table gives winding data.

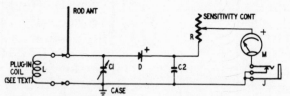

DIODE-TYPE FIELD-STRENGTH METER (Fig. 907)

Resistor: R—1,000-ohm wirewound pot
Capacitors: C1—100-μμf miniature variable (National UM-100 or equivalent); C2—.001-μf 500-volt mica
Coils: see table
Detector: 1N56-A diode
Miscellaneous: M—0-1-ma dc meter; J—closed-circuit phone jack; antenna

Fig. 907. *Circuit of completely self-contained field-strength meter.*

A 2- to 3-foot rod or whip antenna provides sufficient signal pickup for most applications.

The high-conduction 1N56-A germanium diode provides a high ratio of dc output to rf input. Potentiometer R serves as a sensitivity control by permitting adjustment of the amount of direct current flowing through the milliammeter.

When headphones are plugged into jack J, the additional resistance due to the phones in series with the meter will invalidate the meter calibration. The meter deflection therefore is only *relative* when the headphones are plugged in for aural monitoring. When they are removed, the jack automatically restores the meter circuit. A calibrated output rf signal generator may be employed to calibrate the dial of tuning capacitor C1 for frequency and the scale of the milliammeter for microvolts or millivolts of signal strength at a selected setting of R.

Table I—FIELD-STRENGTH METER COILS

.8–3.5 mc	155 turns of No. 34 enameled wire closewound.
3–13 mc	41 turns of No. 24 enameled wire spaced to 1 inch.
10–44 mc	$10\frac{1}{2}$ turns of No. 24 enameled wire spaced to $\frac{5}{8}$ inch (each on 1″ diameter form).
38–150 mc	Hairpin loop of No. 14 bare copper wire $1\frac{3}{4}$ inches high (including portion in base pins of coil form) with $\frac{1}{2}$ inch between legs of hairpin.

For stability, the instrument must be assembled solidly in a metal case, with one circuit point grounded as shown in Fig. 907.

Television antenna compass

The conventional TV antenna orientation meter consists of two parts: a diode rectifier capacitance-coupled to the video electrode (grid or cathode) of the picture tube right at the set, and a dc microammeter which is transported to the roof and is connected to the diode output through a long two-wire line. Many service technicians prefer the compass to a field-strength meter as an indicating instrument for placing and orienting antennas because it operates in conjunction with the receiver to be used with the antenna. Although the antenna compass has been in existence for 6 years, very little has been done to improve it.

The compass described here is eight times more sensitive than the conventional type. It has a more rugged indicating meter and loads the TV receiver less. Only 25 microamperes dc output from the pickup diode will deflect the milliammeter full scale. A single 1.5-volt size-D flashlight cell powers the amplifier, but this need for dc voltage is no inconvenience since the cost of replacing this cell is low and (due to the low full-signal drain of 3 ma) over 1,000 hours of life can be expected on a basis of 8 hours of continuous use per day.

The pickup section (see Fig. 908) consists of C1 and C2, a 1N54 diode and R1. These are mounted in a small box but might also be arranged in a probe. The video signal is picked up through clips connected to receiver ground and to video pins 2 or 11 of the picture-tube socket. The dc output of the pickup section is fed to a two-prong chassis type male plug.

A two-wire line, which can be a length of lamp cord or 300-ohm ribbon, is run from the pickup box plug to the corresponding plug in the remote meter box. On each end of this line there is a female receptacle for connection with the male plugs.

The meter box contains the transistor amplifier circuitry, milliammeter and flashlight cell. The amplitude of the incoming direct current, and accordingly the meter swing, is adjusted by R2. The meter is set initially to zero with R3.

With R2 set to its "zero"-resistance (maximum-sensitivity) position, 2.82 volts peak rf input to the diode circuit will provide full-scale deflection of the meter. When R2 is at its "maximum"-resistance (lowest-sensitivity) setting, approximately 100 volts peak rf will be required.

Since there are no tube heaters to warm up, the instrument is ready to operate as soon as the on-off switch is closed. This makes the instrument as easy to use as a nonelectronic meter.

Temperature changes which reach the interior of the transistor will cause the no-signal meter current to change. Heat increases the current. The no-signal transistor collector current (initially about 10 microamperes) doubles approximately for each 18°F increase in temperature. This means that the meter must be reset to zero as the ambient temperature grows hotter or colder. However, the drift is not severe in normal field service. Furthermore, if the meter is not reset, an initial deflection slightly off zero will not detract from the usefulness of the compass. For these reasons, the circuit has not been complicated nor its power drain increased by including temperature-compensating gimmicks.

The diode pickup circuit (pickup box) is connected to the output of the receiver video channel by connecting the lower clip to receiver ground and the upper clip to the picture-tube grid or cathode, whichever element receives the signal. If a sharp-pointed upper clip is used, the point will puncture the insulation of the video lead, obviating the need to clip to the picture-tube socket. Some of the modern, series-heater TV receivers operate with a hot chassis; that is, the chassis is connected *directly* to one side of the power line. Unless an isolating transformer is used when checking these receivers with any type of instrument used outdoors, the operator must exercise more than ordinary caution to protect himself from dangerous 60-cycle electric shock. *The two instrument boxes are not connected to any part of the circuitry.* The instrument and receiver are switched into operation and the antenna is positioned and rotated for maximum deflection of the meter. When signal pickup is sufficient to slam the pointer, reduce the sensitivity with R2.

The circuit is not critical and the layout is flexible.

The pickup section is built in an aluminum box 2 x 2 x 1½ inches. Two insulated binding posts receive the clip leads from

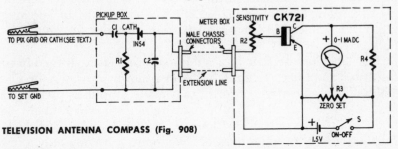

TELEVISION ANTENNA COMPASS (Fig. 908)

Resistors: R1—33,000 ohms; R2—250,000 ohm pot with switch; R3—1,000 ohm wirewound pot; R4—15,000 ohms
Capacitors: C1—250-μμf mica; C2—.002-μf mica
Transistor: CK721

Socket: Transistor
Diode: 1N54
Miscellaneous: M—0—1-ma dc meter; 2—2-pole polarized male plugs; 2—2-pole polarized female receptacles; 2 binding posts; 1 size D flashlight battery

Fig. 908. *Circuit of sensitive electronic compass for use in orienting television antennas.*

the TV set. A two-prong male plug is mounted in the top of this box for plug-in connection to the outgoing line.

The transistor in the meter box is mounted by soldering its three pigtails (each cut to a length of ¾ inch) to the terminals of a three-lug, insulated terminal strip. When soldering the transistor and diode leads, hold each lead with pliers to remove the heat. The flashlight cell is held to the bottom of the box with a short strap. Leads are soldered directly to this cell, since replacement is infrequent.

When wiring the instrument, watch the polarities of the diode, transistor, meter and battery. Connect each of these components exactly as shown in the diagram. The two male plugs are polarized; that is, each has one large and one small prong. This prevents plugging in the interconnecting line in the wrong direction.

As much as 150 feet of lamp cord, 300-ohm ribbon or flexible

151

coaxial line have been used successfully with this type of instrument.

Transistor sound-survey meter

Fig. 909-a shows the circuit of a sensitive sound-survey meter. This instrument can be built small enough to be held in the hand during use. The layout consists of a crystal microphone, high-gain transistorized audio amplifier, and rectifier-type indicating meter. Sounds reaching the microphone produce a meter deflection proportional to the intensity of the sound. This instrument may be used for noise-level checking, sound studies, and as an applause meter. It is operated from a single, self-contained 1½-volt flashlight cell.

The amplifier section is a subminiature 4-stage R-C-coupled transistor amplifier (Centralab TA-11), shown separately in Fig. 909-b. The advantage of this ready-made amplifier package is that it is much smaller than a comparable unit which might be home built. It is only 1.175″ long, 0.665″ wide, and 0.250″ thick. Furthermore, it supplies most of the circuitry, leaving only a few connections to complete the instrument.

In the instrument circuit, the amplifier output is matched to the meter circuit through a small input transformer, T, connected backward to obtain a stepdown ratio. The meter circuit is composed of diode D, CALIBRATION control R2, and the 0–1 dc milli-ammeter, M. With R1 set for maximum gain and R2 set to zero (or lowest obtainable resistance), an input signal of only 200 μv rms at input terminals 1 and 2 deflects the milliammeter to full scale. R1 allows the gain to be set at various levels corresponding to sound ranges. R2 is for initial standardization and recalibration.

Initial testing

(1) Set R2 to its zero-resistance position. (2) Set R1 for maximum gain. (3) Whistle sharply, noting that meter M deflects. (4) While whistling a sustained note at uniform volume, reduce the setting of R1, noting that the meter reads progressively lower as the control is turned down.

After this rough check, the instrument will be satisfactory for comparative measurements. For example, to use as an applause meter, point the microphone toward the audience and have everybody applaud as loudly and evenly as possible. During this noise, adjust R1 for exactly full-scale deflection of the meter. This corresponds to 100% audience response (1 on the meter scale).

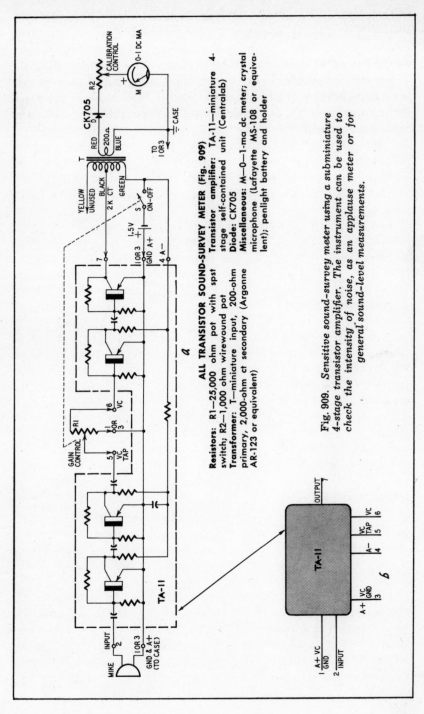

ALL TRANSISTOR SOUND-SURVEY METER (Fig. 909)

Resistors: R1—25,000 ohm pot with spst switch; R2—1,000 ohm wirewound pot
Transformer: T—miniature input, 200-ohm primary, 2,000-ohm ct secondary (Argonne AR-123 or equivalent)

Transistor amplifier: TA-11—miniature 4-stage self-contained unit (Centralab)
Diode: CK705
Miscellaneous: M—0—1-ma dc meter; crystal microphone (Lafayette MS-108 or equivalent); penlight battery and holder

Fig. 909. Sensitive sound-survey meter using a subminiature 4-stage transistor amplifier. The instrument can be used to check the intensity of noise, as an applause meter or for general sound-level measurements.

Subsequent applause may be read in percentage. Thus, 0.4 corresponds to 40% response.

For more accurate sound measurements, the meter scale may be calibrated in decibels and gain control R1 provided with a db range scale by standardizing this instrument against a professional sound-level meter (such as General Radio Type 1551-A) or sound-survey meter (such as General Radio Type 1555-A) under the same noise conditions.

index

155

PRINTED IN THE UNITED STATES OF AMERICA